what she's having

what she's
having

STORIES OF
WOMEN AND FOOD

First published in Great Britain in 2021 by Dear Damsels

Collection © Dear Damsels, 2021

Illustrations © Molly Alessandra Cooper, 2021

'M.F.K. and Me' © Ansa Khan, 2021
'Remedies for Loss of Appetite' © E.V. Somerville, 2021
'Starter' © Hannah Lawrence, 2021
'We Ate Tupperware Meals in the Language of Grief' © Grace Safford, 2021
'Eating by Hand' © Syeda Salmah, 2021
'Aprikosen, Marillen' © Maria Ilona Moore, 2021
'Dad is Dead Mom Sold the Chickens' © Paula Hilton, 2021
'Prison Cake' © Candy Ikwuwunna, 2021
'A Crab for One' © Kate Young, 2021
'Honey Cake' © Amy Feldman, 2021
'An Apple Pie Life' © Tutku Barbaros, 2021
'Feast or Foe' © Ettie Bailey-King, 2021
'Love is ... L'Amore é' © Lucy Porter, 2021
'Of Blood and Blooming Flowers' © Alice Slater, 2021
'Creatures of Habit' © Terri-Jane Dow, 2021
'Life is Still' © Sorcha Collister, 2021

2

ISBN 978-1-8381-6610-6

Printed and bound in Great Britain by Clays Ltd, Elcograf S.p.A.

Dear Damsels
www.deardamsels.com

For our readers, who made this book happen.
Help yourself to seconds.

CONTENTS

EDITORS' LETTER

Dear reader,

There are many subjects we could have chosen for our second collection of fiction, non-fiction and poetry. In the end, the choice was easy. We love reading what women have to say about food, and the fact this book has made its way into your hands suggests you are as interested in the subject – eating it, cooking it, sharing it – as we are.

When we think about food, we think about our everyday routines: meal-times, snack times, just-one-more-bite times; the stack of plates to be washed up at the end of each day. Food is universal, an aspect of modern life we all have in common.

But what we feed ourselves is also incredibly personal. Recipes become family traditions, favourite meals flavour our memories, and our appetites develop every time we discover something new. Hunger, as well as being a simple need, can also be a complex desire.

The sixteen writers in this collection understand this dichotomy, and every story, essay and poem included here shows how food can help us understand the complexities of who we are – whether it's the joys of an elaborate meal for one, the cultural significance of eating with your hands, or the darker side of cravings. If that's not enough to make you want to dive in, the food these writers are serving up surely will be – including, but not limited to, a juicy apricot, crisp puri, a lovingly crafted carrot cake, and platefuls and platefuls of pasta.

We hope you enjoy this book. Read it over coffee with a slice of something sweet. Read it in the kitchen, one hand near the stove, the other thumbing through these pages. Read it when you have a restless hunger you cannot quite satisfy, and find your appetite in the words of women. We hope it fills you up.

Love,
Abby & Bridie
Co-founders of Dear Damsels
Editors of *What She's Having*

NOTES ON CONTENT

REMEDIES FOR LOSS OF APPETITE
Alcohol, body image, diet culture

STARTER
Alcohol

WE ATE TUPPERWARE MEALS IN THE LANGUAGE OF GRIEF
Death, illness

DAD IS DEAD MOM SOLD THE CHICKENS
Death

PRISON CAKE
Body dysmorphia, body image, eating disorder

A CRAB FOR ONE
Alcohol

AN APPLE PIE LIFE
Alcohol, death

FEAST OR FOE
Body image

LOVE IS...L'AMORE É
Death

OF BLOOD AND BLOOMING FLOWERS
Alcohol, blood, body image, diet culture

CREATURES OF HABIT
Body image, death

in the kitchen

Feeding yourself, finding your appetite

M. F. K.
AND ME

ANSA KHAN

From my parents I inherited many wonderful things, of varying degrees of utility: a keen sense of right and wrong; small shoulders; the ability to say 'cat' and 'it's raining' in Pashto; an emotional attachment to comedies made in the eighties. A love of cooking was not among these gifts. My mother and father both cooked some-times, but whatever alchemy by which friends now call their parents for ad-hoc cooking advice, have their gran's biscuit recipe, or base their understanding of how to host a dinner party on what they saw their parents do, didn't happen in my house.

My parents, a nurse and a doctor, worked full time and on shifts, and we ate a lot of microwave meals. (As a child, drawn in by the warm glow of the lamp of the microwave, I used to press my face to the glass and watch the plate go round – very soothing, but maybe not a good idea.) I now often find myself in social settings quite different to the ones I grew up in, and mostly that's cool. I've learned how to pronounce Glyndebourne, that *Midnight's Children* is overrated, and have you read *Shame*? But it took me a while to realise how much my relationship to food and cooking was a little bit of home that I carried with me.

Don't worry: this isn't a lament about growing up in a household that didn't have dinner parties. To say that there are worse things is an understatement of offensive proportions. It's just that when you don't grow up with this stuff, around a particular way of thinking and talking about food, there's a certain amount of learning on the job to be done.

And I am not now completely hopeless, but my education about the joy that can come from cooking for yourself, for others, from having people over for dinner, and in general feeding the ones you love, came later in life.

The polite thing to do in return for all the hard work my parents put in to making sure that my sister and I grew up as members of the middle class, into which neither of them had been born, would have been to become a lawyer or doctor. To the surprise of my father, though, who perhaps hadn't realised how good a job he'd done of ensuring our assimilation, I went into the arts. What followed was an immersion in a world where bread is baked at home, guests are entertained over dinner, chefs are known by name and food writers by their headshots in the weekend papers.

When I first came across the concept of 'food writing', I assumed it wasn't for me; I just couldn't imagine being that interested in food, or interested in it in that way. The copy of M. F. K. Fisher's *The Gastronomical Me* that ended up in my hands did so by accident, and was put there by somebody else. I was fairly confident that I would dip in, conclude that it had very little to say about my life, that there was nothing to distinguish her from any other writer who'd ever expressed love for a crisp bread crust, and be on my way.

In fact, Fisher specifically defends herself from people like me in her preface – people who might have the limited view that to write about food is to write about only that. For Fisher, our needs 'for food, security and love' are indistinguishable from one another, and hence inseparable. So, when she writes about hunger, she is 'really writing about love and the hunger for it, and warmth and the love of it and the hunger for it. . .'

I was sold. Fisher writes about food and cooking, yes, but what lurks beneath it all is a concern with our wants and needs as humans, and that's something I'm definitely interested in reading about.

There is also of course the dazzling writing, the incredible pathos with which she describes even those characters with only walk-on parts. But, if I'm honest, what pleased me most, in true narcissistic fashion, was the discovery that both Fisher and I spent a period of our early twenties living in eastern France, in Dijon. Now, if when I say Dijon the first thing that comes to mind is mustard, let me do you a favour: by far the best thing Dijon has to offer a student on an Erasmus year is crème de cassis: a liqueur made from blackcurrants. Did you know that the cocktail, Kir, is named after Félix Kir, former mayor of Dijon? Did you also know that you can add cassis to *any* wine, *any* one-euro-something bottle of wine, and it's instantly delicious? I hope this information reaches you in time to be useful in your life.

Unsurprisingly Fisher and I were in Dijon for very different reasons. She travelled there in 1929 with her first husband, Al Fisher, who was studying for his doctorate at the Université de Bourgogne – the same institution to which I, seventy-six years later, would turn up with a suitcase, nowhere to live, and an earnest desire to improve my spoken French.

Dijon was not my first choice. It is a very lovely medieval town, but not the first place a twenty-one-year-old thinks of when planning her year abroad. However, the language school in Paris that I'd found online and to which I had paid a small but not insignificant deposit turned out not to exist, so I took one of the last placements on offer from my university and booked a train ticket.

Fisher describes her time in Dijon as one of gastronomical excess, where she and Al spent time eating with people of 'almost every class'. 'Most of our orgies were voluntary,' she explains, 'but even so I doubt if more jaded livers than ours could have stood the thousand bilious blows we dealt them.'

Shamefully (and regretfully for my final French oral grade), my society was largely limited to other students from the University of Manchester, but we too dealt our livers a good few bilious blows. If there were orgies, I wasn't invited.

When M. F. K. Fisher arrived in Dijon, she was newly married, happy and in love. Describing the difficulty involved in learning how to shop and prepare food for herself and Al – how to have salad when there's no fridge, how to buy meat and cheese and butter – Fisher concedes that she wouldn't do it now, but then, 'in the town I loved and with the man I loved, it was fine.'

I was . . . less happy in love, is perhaps the phrase I'm looking for. This was in the early days of Facebook, so if I tell you that it was 'complicated', you might know what I mean. It suffices to say that I had been in what I suppose geometrically speaking was a love triangle but was in fact less exciting than that, involving a girlfriend, a boyfriend, and the girl he was seeing. There would be some reasignment of roles before the year was out.

Dijon would, however, provide the basis of a much longer-lasting relationship, because it was there that I met my friend Rose.

I had only been there a couple of days when I happened to bump into a student I recognised from Manchester who was having a drink with someone else from our course. That someone else told us he was planning to meet a friend and would we like to come along? We met Rose in an internet cafe and then sat in a square for a drink. I remember that she was wearing jeans so ripped I saw more knee than denim. Rolling her own cigarette in that square in Dijon, I think I was slightly scared of her, but in that way that happens when you meet someone who will become a friend and are already a little in love with.

What initially impressed me most about Rose was her apparent ability to let the small things slide. She cared about the important things: books, politics, climate change – perhaps her most enduring legacy has been my conversion to vegetarianism for environmental reasons. But when it came to convention, she didn't seem to get hung up on things that would have had me in knots. To me, she seemed fearless, and one place this was particularly apparent was when it came to food.

Like many of us, Rose lived in a small apartment that was essentially two rooms: the bedroom/living room/kitchen/dining room and the bathroom. One day early in the year, after lectures, we headed back to her flat for lunch. We made guacamole. Now I write that, it doesn't sound revolutionary, but you have to understand that the idea of making – from scratch, at home something – that had formerly only existed in small bowls in Mexican restaurants or in plastic tubs, was mind-blowing. The idea that making it might be as easy as buying the ingredients and having a go, was completely alien. We made it with raw red onions and tomatoes cut into very small pieces. I've since learnt that the jury is still out on whether tomatoes should be in guacamole, but at the time it all seemed inspired. I have no idea what we had with it; perhaps we just ate it with spoons.

Rose also introduced me to the concept of a fried-egg sandwich for lunch – a dish that the waiters at the nearby Le Temps des Ducs restaurant, where we sometimes went for lunch, seemed very reluctant to recreate for her. Each time we went, Rose would order a '*croque madame sans jambon*': a ham-and-cheese sandwich with an egg on top, without ham. I don't know if you have any experience of asking waiters to amend the recipe of a dish by removing one of the key elements; one often receives a little push-back.

At Christmas we decided to pool our resources and make a feast. We all agreed to make a dish at home, before taking it to the flat of our only friend who had enough room for us all. The problem was that only two among us – including the friend with the large enough apartment – had ovens, and the preparation of Christmas dinner tends to be oven-orientated. In the end we devised a plan: I would walk to Rose's where I would help her assemble potato dauphinoise. We would then transport the half-cooked dish to the home of the second oven-owner – the sliced boiled potatoes slosh-ing in cream as we went – where we would bake the potatoes and make the nut roast. The nut roast ready and the potato dauphi-noise baked, we'd then all head to the party. The problem was, we didn't know how long making nut roast takes, and it turns out it takes ages. Instead of using canned tinned tomatoes, the recipe I'd found suggested steaming large tomatoes to loosen the skins, peeling them, then chopping them yourself. This would be fine except it's very hard to do anything but mash tomatoes when they're boiled, covered in scalding water and you're already an hour late for dinner.

When we eventually arrived, I don't remember our lateness being a problem. We were at that stage of adulthood where any latent sense of propriety hasn't really kicked in yet. I do remember that the nut roast was delicious. At a late stage – possibly as we were waiting for the burns from the boiling tomatoes to cool – Rose had thrown in some chilli, adding a kick to what was otherwise essentially brown stodge.

The lack of an oven was also the impetus for my other favourite group culinary memory. For a while there was an ongoing joke: someone would ask 'what's the only dessert you can make without an oven?' to which the correct answer would be 'a cheesecake'. I now know that this is not true, or indeed really a joke, but at the time our repertoires were as limited as our appliances. It was also a good reason to eat a lot of cheesecake. I was leaving halfway through the year in order to fulfil the Spanish-speaking requirement of my degree. At my leaving party, Rose presented me with a cheesecake decorated with my name written in lemon curd. It was beautiful.

It was not long before cooking felt less daunting; I was encouraged by the fact that there didn't seem to be a wrong way to do things. I developed some odd quirks: I would never buy onions, only shallots, as they seemed more manageable. I would make broccoli soup with an entire block of blue cheese (it was as delicious as you'd expect). The layout of my very small flat meant that I could see the hob from the shower, so in an effort to multitask, I would often put things on to boil then go for a wash. Soon I was eager to try cooking for other people too.

Entertaining was also high on Fisher's list of priorities in Dijon, once she and Al moved into their own apartment; it's a mark of their ambition that they buy 'four plates and four forks, instead of two'. I love the moment of discovery when, unlike Al who seems more concerned with what's proper and correct, Fisher decides that 'it is foolish and perhaps pretentious and often boring, as well as damnably expensive, to make a meal of six to eight courses just because the guests who are to eat it have always been used to that many'. I'm very much in agreement with her here, although noone to my knowledge has come to my house expecting six to eight courses. People who didn't like her approach of offering just two or three 'plentiful' and 'interesting' things were welcome not to come again: 'And if they aren't satisfied, let them stay away from our table, and our leisurely comfortable friendship at that table.'

The most memorable meal I served for others in Dijon was a kind of medley of different curries, all prepared on my two-ring hob. I don't recall what carbohydrates I offered as I definitely wouldn't have been brave enough to make rice, but I do remember that one of the dishes had banana in it. I had only one chair and a futon, which was permanently employed as my bed. In order to host, then, I pushed everything to the side of the room and put my duvet on the floor. The pans went in the middle (by the time people got served, they were definitely no longer hot) and everyone sat in a circle around them. As far as I remember it was a roaring success.

What was wonderful about having people round and serving them food I'd cooked was the informality of it. It seemed such a miracle that I, whose culinary exploits had previously been confined to omelettes, or pasta and jars of Dolmio, was cooking for people. Entertaining for them, even. Whether the food was sophisticated enough or my guests were impressed with their surroundings seemed irrelevant.

Fisher and Al eventually leave Dijon. They do a kind of moonlight flit, though they settle up with their landlord first. The freedom and creativity Fisher found in cooking for others didn't mean that there weren't lots of other social hoops she had to jump through while they were there; she isn't yet, when we see her in Dijon, a 'Faculty Wife' with all the responsibilities that entails, but she is on her way. She has to go to tea with her 'almost-colleagues'. Al delivers a 'masterly and amusing' defence of his thesis, and suddenly all the grandees of Dijon who wouldn't previously have given them the time of day, want to have them over for dinner, to 'bestow the accolade of their social recognition'.

The heavy food and heavy conversation prove too much for the couple, who flee to Strasbourg. (In a further strange coincidence, Strasbourg was also the setting for a particularly romantic moment in my young life, involving a French exchange and a moonlit riverside stroll with a young man from Guildford called Ian, but that is perhaps a story for another day.)

I only spent six months in Dijon – not long enough to meet any grandees – and yet I'm still talking about it. When I went back to Manchester in the autumn, I lived with people I'd met there, Rose among them. Along with late nights in the library, cooking became a prominent feature of my final year. Important discoveries included:

- That as well as guacamole, you can also make hummus
- That toasted seeds enliven the blandest soup
- That nothing is made worse by adding grilled halloumi
- That cheesecakes can also be baked.

There was also the time I discovered how to make pastry and then made it incessantly for a month. And the time we tried to make vegan sausages and they ended up looking like brown, lumpen— Well, you can probably imagine.

The above might not sound miraculous to you, but you have to appreciate how exciting this is to someone who had never really cooked, who didn't know how fun it could be, and also how *possible* it was.

*

Dijon is only an interlude for Fisher and Al; they leave Europe and return to the US. Their marriage also comes to an end. Chexbres, Fisher's second love, her great love, appears in the book suddenly. We leave her and Al aboard a ship leaving Europe, and then meet her again as she's travelling to France with Chexbres and his mother – already aware that she'd like to spend the rest of her life with him.

The world that Fisher builds with Chexbres is different: they buy a house in Switzerland, start a phenomenal-sounding garden and decide to cook and serve themselves. Fisher notes that others are shocked at this, it being 'not becoming to our station'. One gets the impression that with Chexbres, Fisher had fun. The modifications they make to the house are 'impractical for anyone but us'. There is an elaborate ruse involving concealing the dinner they have cooked from very hungry guests until the last minute, and shared jokes that leave the pair 'helpless with amusement'.

I knew from Bee Wilson's introduction that Fisher's happiness with Chexbres was limited: he killed himself in 1941 after a debilitating illness that left him in agony. The Second World War also begins to loom as the dates of Fisher's entries get closer and closer to 1939. At one point Chexbres takes three Spanish loyalists out to dinner, while Fisher serves supper to several 'Fascists from Rome, one of them a priest and all of them convinced that Communists were their personal as well as national enemies'. Fisher refers to the 'complications, political, national, religious, even racial' that she saw around her, but it seems that their personal impact on her was limited. It is instead Chexbres' illness which turns them both into 'very live ghosts . . . safely dead', compared to those for whom tragedy in the form of the war was about to hit.

My edition of *The Gastronomical Me* is now filled with Post-it notes marking the passages I loved or the ones that seem to be the heart of the book. The story begins with Fisher's childhood, and ends with her in Mexico. Most of the Post-its fall in and around the time she spent in Europe, but my favourite line comes after she has returned to the US with Al. Once back in California, Fisher tries and fails to recreate the cauliflower casserole that she made often while they were in Dijon. She writes that the difference lies in the ingredients, but she also suggests that they – she and Al – are changed, too: 'I could concoct a good dish, still . . . but it was never so innocent, so simple . . . and then where was the crisp bread, where was the honest wine? And where were our young uncomplicated hungers, too?'

I don't know if the time I spent in Dijon learning to cook was 'uncomplicated'; if anything, life makes a bit more sense today than it did then. Sure, I cook now; it's mostly a pretty organised, sensible affair involving recipes taken from the pages of the Saturday *Guardian*, or from a book featuring photographs of food served in tastefully distressed tins. I've julienned courgettes, de-seeded pomegranates, baked brioche in almond milk; I know how to talk the talk, if you know what I mean. Mostly my lack of, shall we say, foundational knowledge, manifests in a dearth of common sense in the kitchen. I'm bad at slicing, at knowing how long things take to cook. It often takes me a few goes to get the size of the saucepan right, which is a delight for the person doing the washing up. I'm intimidated by long recipes, or things you have to make a day in advance. I didn't season anything before the age of twenty-nine, yet my friends and loved ones – out of loyalty or gratitude – ate my bland creations regardless.

And, while I no longer invite people to eat curry off a duvet on the floor, I still maintain that represents a form of 'leisurely comfortable friendship', if not love, even.

REMEDIES FOR LOSS OF APPETITE

E.V. SOMERVILLE

Go to bed with a single
Breadcrumb beneath your pillow, sleepyhead; dream
of it blooming into a plump loaf,
Mourn when you rise to find it in the morning; Unrisen.

OR

Rest both fists beside your plate,
(ignore any absurd or disconcerting words heard flying around
   the table)
No, clench your cutlery, till you no longer feel it digging into
   your skin
No one is really hungry when they're angry
But as the tension subsides your stomach will rumble to tell you
You haven't touched your food.

OR

Pick a clover under a full moon (a three-leaf will do)
Press it into your right palm with your left thumb,
Thank either the Father, the Son and the Holy Spirit
Or else Beyoncé, Kelly and Michelle,
Or name your gods
by whatever it is that moves you
Thank any of them
With all your heart
That you only ever had an empty plate
at the end of a meal and
never at the start.

OR!

Pull a plump plum tomato from the vine when the host
    isn't looking
It smells divine! (Which it is)
Is it anyone's *business*
if an empty belly needs
to pinch one, just a taste of that fierce red sun?
You feel a little naughty but a rush like that is harmless,
and does you good
And so it should!
In the evening, your fingers seek something fresh, or salted,
    or doughy,
and know that it too will not just sustain but satisfy you.

SO

Abandon what parents seemed to tell their babes, their bairns,
    sweet cariad! Oour ked,
Through the nineties;
That There Are ChildrenStarvingHungryInAfrica.
    Those Children Have
Nothing
To
Eat!
When you recall all this;
their call to Refuse defeat and Consume your portion completely
You may parcel it up
– with the best intention but *replete* naivety –
Declare: 'Anywhere in the Third World'
Scrawled onto the warm, weighty envelope which holds your
    dinner
In its sealed sandwich bag
Once you've paid the postage,
Then you let it go.

OR

Sign up for a marathon; affording you a pious way to decline
the shortbread and home-bakes constantly offered around
    the staffroom
When you reach the finish line,
Your cravings may not return to you
but your hunger is sure to.

OR

Cry your heart out!
Exhaust yourself to sleep
Leap out of your skin at the unwelcome din of your
    phone alarm
Startled but unharmed
Jumpstart yourself with hot water and lemon to calm yourself
You have nourished one part of yourself,
Now restore your energy spent, no guilt,
No resentment for calories or cost,
What was once lost *can be rebuilt.*

OR

Drink glass after glass of water
Till your belly sloshes
And the desire for bread becomes
unarguable.

OR

Drink glass after glass of beer
until you speak no sense
Then make your wobbled way home
As the desire for something to fill your void becomes
    unavoidable
Start with bread and butter
It can't hurt
Mutter a grace if you can't find the courage to say one and

if you're stuck, thank the god damn cow, or the almost abstract
    wheat plough, something, someone.
Take even a few small bites.
Get to bed before 1a.m.

OR

Call your grandmother
Ask her to teach you how to get her chicken recipe – with the
    ambiguous White Sauce and just a little sweetness – just right
Even though you know it by heart,
Then, in an empty house,
cook through the night.

OR!

Teach a child to eat their greens
But sneak yourself a Milky Way when they're not paying
    attention
It's easier than explaining everything – including but not
    limited to –
How your tummy rumbles now for something to steady you
Including, but not only
How this small child has worn you out.

OR

Dance so long
So hard
That the rumble of your tummy is heard above the drums

You might forget for a moment there, but the hunger will come
    back to you again
when it's good and ready.

OR

Steady the bookshelf
Fix it against the wall
I have learned the gory way that things can fall from all sorts
    of heights
So when the shelves are fixed in their proper place
Trace your fingers along that river of spines and find
Whichever book has the most beautiful images
to whet your appetite
Cook by picture, in spite of all those directive words,
    ignore them,
Invent some bold, absurd concoction
for the sheer delight of it,
it might taste shite but whatever
Doesn't poison you
Only makes you a better chef in the end,
and if,
If *all* of that fails
Pretend.
For just long enough to get some roughage in you;
To digest *something* to restore your strength
For just long enough to see sense.
Come sit with me,
Ready to receive, exhale, take a load off your feet.

Every one of your ancestors has gone to great lengths to get here.
Come, Beloved,
Eat.

STARTER

HANNAH LAWRENCE

I don't know if she's heard. She's certainly not mentioned it, but then she wouldn't. I've thought about saying something about it, just an off-hand thing, you know, to see if there's any indication in her response that gives it away. But then I think, don't torture yourself. Ultimately you'll never know and perhaps that's best.

She was the first person I ever called my 'best friend'. Probably because we met at an age when it was acceptable to demarcate your friends through that kind of hierarchy. I guess what I learnt is that even with the most explicit label in the world, you can't always prevent friendships changing.

Sometimes I'll be standing at the kitchen counter, waiting for a piece of toast to ping, when she'll come and stand next to me, reaching down for something in the fridge, and I'll become suddenly aware of our bodies next to one another, of just how much we've grown.

*

The thing binding us together sits in the kitchen, day after day, waiting to be fed. When it was gifted to us by a mutual friend I'd been slowly falling out of touch with I assumed it wouldn't be me looking after it. I'm known for being the absent-minded one after all, as she's so fond of reminding me. She's always been the leader, the practical, organised one. I thought she'd take charge of this demanding sourdough starter and I could sort of relinquish responsibility, but it doesn't seem to have worked out like that. Instead I seem to have taken it on as my own, looking after it day after day, doing all the research on what it needs and how best to look after it, feeding it just the right amount.

I pick up the bubbling mass, the circular pockets of air squashed up against the smooth curve of the Kilner jar. I pour 125ml of water into the open jar and gently spoon in 100g of flour, stirring the claggy mixture and smearing the thick nebulous mush off the spoon with my finger.

She comes in and peers over my shoulder as I'm scraping the thick white substance onto the side of the jar.

'So that's what you do with it, is it?' She walks over to the sink and starts filling up her glass. 'Once a day?

'Yeah, for the first seven days. Then you can start baking with it, or you can put it in the fridge and it kind of goes dormant, so you only have to feed it once a week.'

'Why in the fridge?'

'Well, from what I've read online – mostly from Bob in Kentucky who is a keen home baker . . .' My attempt at humour falls into the void between us as she continues to look at me expectantly. 'If you bake a lot you can keep it out on the surface so it's ready whenever you want to use it but then you have to feed it every day.'

She already looks bored, taking a sip from her newly filled glass, and I decide not to go into why you need to feed it at roughly the same time every day and why the difference in temperature affects it and why Bob thinks his loaves work best when he sticks with the same variety of flour.

Occasionally, she'll suddenly take an interest in it – when she's frustrated by something I've said, something I've called her out on, she'll suddenly take on the responsibility, giving it its feed – inevitably feeding it too much, at the wrong time of day, and messing up the schedule. I think she sees it as her way of wrestling back control after some supposed slight but what she doesn't realise is it's wasted on me because I just don't really care. It's no more mine than it is hers, I just look after it better.

I'm not sure if we were ever really the same 'type of person' or whether I was just so enamoured by her that whatever she wanted for herself I wanted for myself too. It's hard to tell exactly when this one way street of admiration got shut off, but it was probably around the time that I realised the reason I was failing to achieve all the things we both wanted in life was because I didn't really want them after all. Now that the commonality and admiration has gone we're awake to the fact that we're two separate people, no longer similar, but united by a joint responsibility for the direction of the other's growth. Now, we're finding our way into a new friendship based on history alone.

The slim margin in which our interests and aspirations overlap has become the core of our friendship, the space where our ability to talk openly to one another still remains untouched. The parts of our lives not covered by this slim margin is vast. It includes love, sex and romance, politics, feminism, marriage, our ultimate life goals, and the morality of swiping aubergines through as onions at the self-checkout. When we stray too far from this slim margin we know we're in uncomfortable territory. The 'not-in-common zone' has all too often led to late night disagreements followed by passive aggressive breakfasts.

I look up from the blender. I can see her lips moving but I can't tell what she's saying over the sound. When it becomes clear it's more than a passing comment I can get away with ignoring I pause it for a second.

'Say that again.'

'Why has sourdough even become such a big thing? It's not even that good.'

'You don't like it?' I ask, wearied by a day of her being constantly contrary.

'Like, it's okay, but it's not worth the price. Have you seen how much they used to charge down at the food market? It's like four pound a loaf. So ridiculous.' She's wearing a pair of slipper socks and twisting on the balls of her feet as she talks, both feet sliding together first left then right. It's something she's done since we were children.

'I guess that's why everyone's making it themselves,' I reply, turning the blender back on before she has time to respond.

I keep it going until she's left the room and I can be sure the conversation is officially over, turning what was meant to be bread-crumbs into dust in the process.

'I guess once we finish that last loaf from the freezer we could try out the starter?' I say, spreading reduced-price margarine across a thin slice of defrosted granary, the sliced sunflower seeds nestled in the dough gazing up at me as the knife passes over them.

There's something about the way the sweetness of the synthetic yellow margarine mingles with the tuna mayonnaise that reminds me of childhood. Cheap tuna-and-cucumber sandwiches handed over the back of the car seat during long journeys. Tuna and sweetcorn on a white bap from a seaside sandwich shop during a school-trip. A tuna salad on brown – no red onions please – from the canteen at Dad's work when he'd take me in for the day during the summer holidays. The more mayo the better. Though there are the Heston Blumenthals of the world poring over their haute cuisine I suspect it's all a ruse. To me, food just doesn't get better than a tuna sandwich on cheap sliced bread, with some worryingly yellow margarine.

I know she hates the smell of it, can't understand how anyone would think it acceptable to eat a tuna sandwich within a one-mile radius of another living, breathing human being. I take myself off to the living room to eat lunch most days.

'I'm never going to say no to a home-baked loaf, but I won't hold my breath,' she replies, twisting the paper label on the end of the tea bag before snapping it off and dumping it in the bin. 'It would be good if you could maybe get round to doing at least one of the things you've been saying you'll do this whole time.'

It's always when we've had a few solid days of getting on that she'll come out with something vaguely cutting, as if the balloon that is our relationship has reached its limit of expansion and there's nowhere else for it to go. She has no other choice but to pop it.

It only happened the once, but it was all I needed.

I was rooting around in the 'cloakroom' – aka, the bedroom of whichever flatmate had drawn the short straw that night and been forced to offer theirs up – for the four-pack of offie lager I'd put under my coat at the beginning of the night. Across the room I could see a woman looking at me, her friend was saying something in her ear but she was looking straight ahead, straight in my direction. I could feel myself getting flustered, still rooting around for the cans that I just couldn't find.

She ended up lending me one of hers, then another. Two cans in, outside by number 42's wheelie bin, she kissed me. At first I drew away and her eyes widened with a look of embarrassment. But the beers were starting to kick in and I leaned forward and kissed her.

Less than twenty minutes later, as she went off to find her friend and get us two more beers, I left without saying goodbye, grabbing my bag from under a mountain of others and slipping out the front door. I went home and lay awake in bed until the sun began to come up, peeking through my curtains like the tide of realisation slowly trickling into my brain.

She walks in as I'm fighting my way through a cloud of flour, the inevitable effect of having a top shelf no-one can properly reach. I start desperately trying to clean up the little specks of white as she makes her way to the sink.

She puts the starter back in the fridge, clearing up around me. I don't say anything, it's not worth it; I'll just take it back out in a minute when she's left the kitchen.

No matter how carefully I spoon the flour onto the scales, small plumes of white are released. They hang in the air for a second, almost defying gravity, before they're gone and there's a fresh white mess on the floor.

The starter and I go through the usual process: 125 ml of water followed by 100 mg flour. The same routine as always. It's like feeding a child.

She clears around me, pottering between the sink and the work surface, ringing out the cloth and spraying antibac dangerously close to the Kilner jar. Like a protective parent I move it to the side.

'Okay, so talk me through exactly what you do again. I want to get on board with this sourdough thing,' she says.

I turn around, slightly shocked. Now that I've taken on the responsibility for the starter I feel possessive over it. I have a sudden reflex that tells me I don't want to share.

The ambulances come almost hourly down the road, sometimes with the siren on, sometimes without. Either way, I see the reflection of the lights flashing on the white wall of the living room as I work or through the gaps in my curtains at night. The ambulances remind me of how good I've got it, relatively speaking. A roof over my head, a job that pays the bills. In this moment, I'm aware of how much there is to be grateful for in that.

We both work at the large kitchen table, day after day. We've become sort of in tune, meal times, tea breaks, almost toilet breaks.

Slowly the distance between us is narrowing with each day that we spend together in the small proximity that is our home. Slowly our conversations have stopped being confined to the past tense, stopped being rooted in historical events from a time when we were both the same 'type of person'. Now we have things in the present to connect over and some of them aren't inconsiderable either. Conversationally they certainly give us good mileage.

We've even started cooking together, which, for me, is quite a big deal. I'm very much a solitary chef; I can't even have music with words on while I cook. If someone comes into the kitchen while I'm

33

making food I feel unsettled by their presence. It makes me insecure about my chopping style and the lack of organisation with which I make meals. I'm not a bad cook but I'd prefer to be judged on my food rather than my presentation in the kitchen.

Our eating habits have changed since the days when our diets consisted mostly of post-school doorstop sandwiches cut from thick, brown loaves in her grandma's kitchen. Now we're making mushroom risotto and warm salads with crusty bread. As we chop orange and yellow tomatoes and thick crusts of stale bread for a tangy panzanella salad, standing side by side against the work surface, I'm struck again by how we've grown. Back then our little bodies sat contentedly side by side, nourished by the starchy goodness of a rural upbringing, as we discussed the minutiae of a world that felt familiar. Now we stand almost six feet tall, reaching away from each other for tastes and flavours that signify to ourselves we've changed; that show how different life beyond the cul-de-sac has made us.

The cooking together naturally results in eating together, which has escalated into watching TV together. The idea of us doing this was pretty unimaginable at the start of all this, particularly because, more often than not, it involved negotiating the 'not-in-common zone'. The prospect of us finding a show that fitted in the slim margin of our common interests seemed impossible but somehow – by which I mean endless hours of scrolling – we've found one that fits comfortably within the small sliver of our common interests.

The little network of gluten squashes beneath my palm as I knead it into a smattering of flour on the work surface, its elasticity proving itself beneath my grip. I'm in a daze from the repetitive motion when she comes in, making me jump slightly as she edges behind me to get to the cupboard.

'Oh sorry, didn't mean to shock you,' she laughs. 'So, the big moment hey?'

'Ha, yeah, something like that.'

I continue staring straight out the window, smushing the tacky dough beneath my dry, floury palms and awkwardly catching a delivery driver's eye as I gaze blankly towards him.

I hear the door close behind her, leaving me to knead in peace. It seems the flour I laid out across the work surface has been absorbed as much by my hands as by the dough. My palms are starting to itch from the dryness.

I keep scooping flour out onto the surface and padding the dough back into the powder until I feel like I'm making it worse. Treating the matte ball of dough with such attentive gentleness I even surprise myself, I tip it into the bowl and cover it with a tea towel. My nurturing has reached a new level.

I have my set-up all complete. A tray of water on the bottom shelf is creating steam in the pre-heated oven. A baking tray, gifted by my mother when I left home clearly knowing one day I'd turn my hand to making bread, is heating through on the top shelf.

Speckles of white flour cover the bottom of the tray in patches. I tip the little uncooked loaf into the tray being careful to disrupt it as little as possible. This sourdough ritual has given me a newfound respect for precision.

I've read enough sourdough blogs to know the final touch of any baker worth their salt is the characteristic slashes in the crust of the bread. Even if it fails to rise, even if it's as hard as a brick, at least it'll have the sourdough slashes.

I guess the chasm between us is why I never told her. It would technically, after all, come under romance, a category strictly relegated to the 'not-in-common zone'. It's tricky territory and one no longer worth venturing into.

Sometimes, I think, surely she knows? Surely she's just keeping it quiet. But then there are other moments where I find myself reflecting and thinking no, there'd be some hint that she knew. I know if it was me I'd have let it slip right away, I've never been good at keeping a secret, but then some people's faces are just better than mine at hiding things. But she can't keep a secret either; it's not that her face gives things away, it's that she can't resist letting everyone know that she knows something they don't.

I've burnt the crust too much and it doesn't look like all the photos online. There's something so solid about sourdough, the outside so dense and crisp that it practically takes a saw to get through, but then, once you do, the inside is so light and airy, like a balloon.

I start slicing through the crisp, shiny crust, breaking into the end of the loaf with the sharpest knife we have.

I leave hers on a plate knowing it would be a mistake to attempt to estimate the exact amount of butter she wants. I watch the little curls of yellow butter disappear as they melt into the hot dough, slipping through to the plate below. I scoop up the plates, knife and butter packet in my arms, the cold aluminium foil resting on the crease of my skin as I carry the precarious pile through to the living room.

'Here it is, the finished product,' she smiles. 'Not bad. Only eight weeks in the making.'

'Just be grateful it didn't cost you four pound.'

'Probably cost us four pound in flour.'

'Wait till you taste it, worth every penny.'

I curl up on the sofa furthest away from the TV as she leans forward on the coffee table to spread thin layers of butter across the nexus of doughy holes in the cooling bread. I can hear her chewing as she works her way through the tough crust. She pauses between mouthfuls, engrossed in the telly. Then she turns to me, waving her buttery fingers at the TV.

'I love how she's bi and it's just like, no big deal,' she says, looking back towards the TV. 'Like it's key to the plot but no drama is made of it. It just is.'

There it is. That's the line. She knows. I knew it and now I, well, know it. I knew she'd never be good enough at hiding it if she did know. I feel myself stiffen.

She curls her right foot further underneath her and looks down at her plate, taking a torn piece of the slice and mopping up the pool of melted butter with the doughy centre.

'I'm so here for it,' she says with a satisfied sigh, licking the butter off her fingers and looking at me slightly doe-eyed before ripping off another piece of the soft dough.

She's doing it, she's stepping out of the slim margin. She's ventured into the vast expanse of the 'not-in-common zone'. It's warmth and acceptance and a complete breach of trust all at once.

WE ATE TUPPERWARE MEALS IN THE LANGUAGE OF GRIEF

GRACE SAFFORD

'People aren't tidy creations to be stacked neatly in Tupperware or poured in pre-measured quantities from a box into the Cuisinart with no spills; everybody alive is a lost and disastrous mess.'

— Joel Derfner

Goulash
A stew of meat and vegetables seasoned with paprika.

Ingredients
2lb ground beef (or alternative)
2 cloves garlic
3 cups water
2 cans tomato sauce (15 ounce cans)
2 teaspoons Italian seasoning

2 teaspoons paprika

2 cups uncooked elbow noodles (macaroni)

1 cup shredded cheese

Salt and pepper, to taste

That's what was in our fridge. Red, thick and viscous – more of a gelatin than a stew – taking up a whole shelf in a blue-and-white Tupperware that was so old the owner didn't care if we gave it back or not. It was the kind of Tupperware that smelled so strongly of plastic you couldn't help but wonder if it was leaking into your food. It was the kind of Tupperware you see in movies, shuffled through hands after funerals between condolences and well-wishes, the kind that neighbours show up with, unannounced, when they've heard someone has died.

I never realised that in real life people give you them before someone dies, too.

'Grace? You can just warm that up for dinner. Grab an apple or something, too. I'll see you tomorrow, okay?' my mother calls from our front door, her plate of goulash half finished – picked at – by the sink.

From my spot on our couch, I want to tell my mother I hate goulash. That I hated it when she made it for a camping trip and I hated it every Fourth of July barbecue. That I really hated it whenever it got slapped on my plate at a potluck or field trip. That I wanted something else, anything else. But she had already closed the door on the way to see her sister in the ICU.

I really tried to be brave, at first. Really. When everything was new and fresh and I was still learning the impact of the acronym ICU, my hand went easily to the fridge. My feet walked to the kitchen and told me I could open my mouth and do what was right.

So many Tupperware meals were entering our home every day and I knew the best thing I could do was to eat them so they didn't go bad. We didn't need any more rotten things in this house.

Minutes after my mother leaves, I open the blue lid. The goulash is so congealed, red and white, tomatoes and pasta, it looks like a bowl of blood and bones, like a deer carcass blown open on the side of the road. Bile forms at the base of my throat, hot and flavourless.

I grab an apple and go to my room.

Shepherd's Pie

A casserole of ground meat and vegetables topped with mashed potatoes.

Ingredients

3 large potatoes, peeled and quartered (to be mashed)
8 tablespoons butter
1 medium onion, chopped
1–2 cups vegetables (peas, carrots, corn)
1lb ground beef (or alternative)
½ cup beef broth
1 teaspoon Worcestershire sauce
Parsley, to taste
Salt and pepper, to taste

The last thing my aunt said to me was, 'I'll tell you when you're twenty-one.' I am now twenty-two.

Yet I'm sixteen when I look at the shepherd's pie taking up yet another shelf in our fridge. I'm sixteen when we all still believe she is going to be okay. I'm sixteen when we still think she is going to tell me her story. It has been only four days since she started her bladder cancer treatment. My mother calls to tell me her sister said she feels bad for all of us. She's the one who gets to sit in bed and be taken care of. We're the ones who have to stand and watch her lose her hair.

I'm sixteen and adulthood still feels a lifetime away.

Maybe that's why I felt justified for refusing to eat our Tupperware meals. Justified for shoving the horrible corn-and-beef concoction to the back of the fridge. My aunt said she was going to be okay so it was okay for me to refuse this lumpy food no one liked. That I didn't like. That my mom barely even registered. That my dad shoved in the microwave after work because food is food as long as he's not hungry afterwards.

I was going hungry – even though I didn't need to be. It had been four days since I'd really had a proper meal. As a teenager I was still a picky eater to the extreme, and casseroles and baked dishes of random ingredients tossed together were at the top of my Do Not Eat list. Even in a time of need, a time when I should have been doing the right thing, I still couldn't bear to throw Do Not Eat foods onto a fork.

But for some reason that's all people knew how to bring us. I think they thought they were bringing us big hearty meals that would last, that could be lost in the fridge for days before we discovered it. *Kindness*. But the only meals I thought were worth saving were my mother's.

My mother knew how to cook. She knew what everyone in the house liked and didn't like. She knew where every spice in her cabinet was even though the shelf looked more like a junk drawer than a kitchen space. She chopped and cleaned carrots in what felt like seconds and somehow always knew what sauce would go well with anything green. I loved to watch her at night, as I sat perched up on the counter despite her glare, smelling the sautéed garlic and peppers that frequented her pans. Sometimes I couldn't help but wonder if my mother was a witch, throwing thyme and sage into her brew. It felt like the only logical answer to the magic of her food on my tongue. Even if I didn't want to eat the foods she was making (which was shamefully often), I still wanted to learn how she knitted her fingers over the stove.

My mother's entire family – a family of three women, no men – were cooks. They all knew that magic. Just like my mother, the place I remember my aunt best is in the kitchen.

It's Thanksgiving. It's Easter. I'm ten. I'm twelve. She's in her small square kitchen leaning up against her concrete counter in a black tank top, watching me fish another Fresca out of her fridge. I think the drinks are just okay, but it's an excuse to get into the kitchen with her and my mother and their mother. To watch them talk about memories I don't have. To watch them make food I won't eat but think looks beautiful under their wizened hands. Their twin hands. Hands honouring traditions I was too young to hold. My aunt is talking about music she loves or students who irritated her in her class. She's pressing her arm against her mother's. She's crimping tinfoil over a ham or a lamb. She's laughing at my mom, her baby sister, for something, everything. She's telling her son to pick his toys up. She's moving her shoulders to a CD her husband has just turned on. She's looking to me and asking me a question like I am an adult like the three of them, like I am at the counter stirring stock or chopping onions. She's smiling at me. She's making me feel like I am a part of something by calling me Grace and calling me smart. She's making me feel more than I am in that moment.

Pushing away the shepherd's pie in our fridge I am lesser. I won't eat it. I throw a tantrum no one will see as I shut the fridge and open the pantry, shaking the hinges. My mother knows what I want to eat and I know what I don't want to eat. I won't eat goulash or shepherd's pie, no matter how kind it is.

I start making PB&Js and wait for my mother to come home and cook something else. She wants to be with her sister and I want my mother to be happy but I also want her to turn on the burner and show me where she keeps her secrets. I want from her in a way I know she cannot give but I want to ask for anyways. I lick condiments on a knife and resolve to wait as long as it takes for something *good*.

Peanut butter starts to taste like a guilt I cannot yet name.

Potato Salad

A salad made from boiled potatoes and mayonnaise.

Ingredients
6 medium Yukon golds, skin on and quartered
3 tablespoons white vinegar
6 green onions, diced
4 hard boiled eggs, peeled
1 ½ cups mayonnaise
1 tablespoon yellow mustard
Paprika, to taste
Salt and pepper, to taste

The day my aunt said her last words to me we'd just had a barbecue on the lake. We were sitting on the front porch of my grandmother's summer rental, avoiding the cigarette smoke curling from the back deck, her arm pressing into mine. My aunt has a white-and-blue

Tupperware in her lap, the sides licked and smeared with mayonnaise and potato skins that look a little too much like our skin. I hadn't eaten any. Potato salad was on my Do Not Eat list.

As the party was winding down we squinted at the sun and swatted at the moths who mistook us for light. I think she was telling me about Vegas. I was still too young to know whether she went every year because she liked to gamble or because she liked to travel.

'Black Jack. I think it's rigged but it's better with . . .' My aunt trails off, laughing to herself as she absently clicks the handles of her Tupperware. She keeps coughing even though there's no reason for her to.

I want to laugh with her too, but her husband comes out from his smoking spot, gently grabbing her elbow to help my aunt up, waving with his free hand to the family watching them from the house.

'Better with what?' I ask, still seated, trying to ignore the knees now crowding around me, watching my aunt slowly walk to her car.

'I'll tell you when you're twenty-one,' she calls, throwing the words over her shoulder.

She waves. I can't tell if she's waving off our conversation or waving goodbye. She would find out she has cancer three days after this conversation.

A week later – a week of my mother leaving and Tupperwares appearing – my dad comes to pick me up from work. I know he has something to tell me because I could have easily walked home. I work sweeping floors at our local general store only a street away.

'Grace.' My dad is looking forward, going ten miles below the speed limit as we near the turn to our road.

'What is it?'

'Your mom is home. She . . . they found more today. More

tumours. They're all over her sister's body. It's . . . it's terminal.'

'Terminal?' I ask it like a question even though I know what the word means.

My dad shifts his truck into gear and pushes on the gas. There is no avoiding going fast on our hill. It's the only way to get up without rolling back down. 'She's going to die. We don't know when . . . she could have a few years . . . but she's not going to make it, Grace.'

'Okay.'

We let that 'okay' hang there until we park. The trip took all of five minutes.

'Your mom is in the living room,' my dad says. 'Try to be strong for her?'

'Okay.'

But when I see my mother sitting on the couch, the same one I sit on day after day watching her open and close the door, we both burst into tears. I crawl into her lap and we both soak each other's hair and mutter words that have no meaning. I think I say I am sorry but I don't know who I am saying it to.

Eventually the crying stops. I finally get a good look at my mother. Her hair is limp, plastered so closely to her head I can see the small points of her freckled ears looking back at me in a way I rarely see. What strikes me most is her chest, the small area just below her neck. The two points under the start of her clavicle bones are sucked in, pushing so far into her body it looks like her skin is trying to take a breath. Later, when I am trying to fall asleep, I will think she looked hollow.

No one knows what time it is but my mother is already thinking about the next morning – her next trip to the hospital. She says she is going to pack for a few days this time. She says she is too tired to eat. My dad says he is too. I say I lost my appetite and we all agree this is a night for sleeping and forgetting.

But I am lying. I have been lying all week as I mixed a spoon in our Tupperware meals to make it look like I'd eaten them. I was hungry. I was so fucking hungry. And all I could think about was how my mother had said 'a few days' and how that meant it was going to be days until she cooked again, more days with a dormant stove, more days filled with plastic, more days of bread and butter and cereal and scrounging.

And I was so fucking hungry.

Baked Macaroni

A baked deep dish of elbow noodles and mixed cheeses.

Ingredients
16 oz elbow macaroni
8 tablespoons butter
⅓ cup all-purpose flour
3 cups whole milk
1 cup heavy whipping cream
4 cups sharp cheddar cheese, shredded
2 cups Gruyère cheese, shredded
Salt and pepper to taste

I hate mac and cheese.

Mac and cheese is an American staple and it's my least favourite food in the world. The only time I despised a food my mother made so much I spit it out into a napkin was when she made baked mac and cheese for one of her birthdays. The colour is unnatural. The shape is too uneven. The smell is too close to something man-made for comfort. The combination of plain pasta and cheese tastes like cardboard. The texture alone is enough to make me refuse any form of baked noodles and cheese for the rest of my life.

When a baked mac and cheese enters our house in a square Tupperware, I ask my father if we can make spaghetti instead.

'Why is the burner just clicking?' I ask my dad, turning the knob again and again on our stove, holding an empty pot in one hand like I was about to bring it down on the appliance if it didn't cooperate.

'It should just turn on,' he says, standing in the entryway of the kitchen, pacing. 'Maybe it's out of gas?'

'I don't think that's how that works.' The stove keeps clicking. 'It *smells* like gas. Like, bad.'

'Try turning it again,' he says, taking another step back.

My father and I both jump as the fire hit the immense amount of gas I had just created in our kitchen. I dropped the pan, patting my face with both hands to check for missing eyebrows.

'I'm getting something out of the fridge,' my father says.

Eventually my hands move from my face to my stomach, holding together the empty space there. I felt betrayed that my father didn't know how to cook but even worse that I shared the same confusion. I was sixteen. I wasn't a child. I was old enough to go on my first date that same summer and drive a car down the interstate much faster than I should have. I should know how to cook. I should be eating more than bread shoved across my scorched tongue when I got hungry at midnight. I should know how to cook.

I wanted being in the kitchen to mean something good again, or at least, what good meant to me.

My father warms up some of the baked macaroni now claiming a corner in our plastic-smelling fridge. When he offers to warm me up a plate I say I am not hungry yet. I will eat later.

After a cup of applesauce and another PB&J, I call my mother. 'How's it going? How is she?'

She sighs. 'I don't know, she's been asleep a lot.'

'What does that mean?'

'I'm not really sure. I think she just needs the rest.'

My mother is the one who sounds like she needs the rest. Her voice sounds so hard yet brittle I barely recognise her even though my phone is telling me who I am speaking to.

I pause for a moment. 'When are you coming home?''

She sighs again, deeper. 'I don't know, honey. Probably tomorrow. I need some more clothes. But then I'll be at the hospital again.'

I bite my tongue, holding in the question I actually want to ask. The reason I called and the reason that hurts my stomach in a way that digs deeper than unwanted foods.

I want to ask my mother if she will cook for me when she gets home. I know I should offer to help her or talk to her but I want to ask if she will make chicken or pasta or pizza or something good and delicious. I want to ask if she will help me. Feed me.

Please feed me. Please feed your terrible daughter. I bite my tongue even harder as she says goodbye.

Broccoli Casserole

A casserole of broccoli, cheese and canned soup.

Ingredients

1 can condensed cream of mushroom soup

½ cup mayonnaise

1 egg, beaten

½ onion, chopped

49

 3 packages frozen chopped broccoli
 1 cup shredded Cheddar cheese (or to taste)
 Salt and pepper, to taste

The call comes at 3 a.m. My dad doesn't need to tell me who it is or what they said. I am crying by the time he hangs up and opens my door.

From the time my aunt started her cancer treatment to the time she died, only about three weeks had passed. Three weeks of coming and going, phone calls and crying, and meals and containers appearing at our door. Three weeks of hunger.

I never went to go visit her because I thought she would have more time. I never said goodbye.

My father and I both wake up early that day with nothing better to do than wait. My mother is coming home. For good this time.

I think my father watched T.V. I think I read a book. Eventually we both just walked around the house, touching surfaces, waiting for my mother to come and touch them too.

At one point, my father finally speaks.

'Remember to support your mom when she gets here, right? Give her what she needs.'

I nod, my heart pinching a bit that he felt like he needed to say those words.

My dad rubs his forehead, smoothing out the lines there with a thumb. 'She's going to need us. That was her sister.'

After hours of wandering, we both drift over to the kitchen. He opens the fridge, absently rummaging and shifting the food without really grabbing any of it.

'I don't know what she's eaten in the past few days,' my dad says, finally wrapping his hands around a broccoli casserole. 'Maybe hospital food, but everyone knows that's really just glorified paste.'

'She hasn't been eating?'

'I don't know. But at least there's food here.'

I run up to my bedroom as he pops the red Tupperware lid.

Mom hasn't been eating. My mother hasn't been eating.

We have food. Dozens of containers of it. And yet I'm not eating out of a childlike protest and my mother hasn't eaten because she was too busy watching her sister die. In my bed, I ask myself if I am the villain of my own story. I wonder if that's how both of our griefs manifested – through food. Only mine was a grief that turned into selfishness to avoid the grief. My mother didn't have that luxury.

Finally, I can hear tyres turning the gravel of our driveway. I'm on the stairs as my mother walks through the front door.

Her face is open. So open. It somehow looks fresh and young in the way her eyes are wide and I can't see the shallow wrinkles usually crinkled next to her nose. Her chin is turned up, the midday sun catching it, causing her skin to glow like burnt honey. There's a little smile on her lips that's spelling the word relief.

'Hey,' I say. I feel stupid the second I say it.

'Hey love,' she says, the same relief spreading from her face to her voice.

'Do you . . . do you need anything?'

She smiles. 'No . . . I just . . . I just want to cook something.'

My hand slips on the banister. 'Oh! Okay, yeah. Okay.'

We both disappear into our rooms. The house smells faintly of cheese and broccoli, but also of chemicals and dry air.

My throat squeezes in a way that feels like it's making room for food, good food, my mother's food, and I—

I feel like shit I feel like shit a privileged shit and I have this strange mixture of sadness and confusion in me and guilt and so much guilt and shame I can't even feel my toes I just feel guilt running in my veins where my blood should be oh god I feel not there at all but incredibly here in this house with silence and food and hurt and I want nothing more than to do the right thing and I don't know why it is so hard to be as good as my mother and my aunt and my aunt is now dead and her sister is here and I feel like shit because of what I am asking from my mother and what she can no longer ask of her sister of what she no longer has and the emptiness in her stomach that does not come from food but speaks in the language of grief when all I can do is feel like shit feel like utter shit and speak in the language of me of me of me of me of me of me of always me and not her and just let me be good just let me be good good good good—

The sound of metal and moving feet pulls me out of my bed into our home.

I slowly walk down our stairs again, planting myself a few paces outside of the kitchen – in the place where my father watched me burn the air. My mother is standing in the middle of it all, looking at the clock on the stove, pulling out mixing bowls and stock and bread. Nothing in the kitchen looks like a recipe, but she's already turning on the stove – the burner catching in one stroke.

And for once, I am not hungry.

I swallow. 'Mom?'

She keeps looking at the clock. 'I'm making dinner.'

I don't say it's midday. I don't try to stop her slow-moving hands. I just unglue myself from my spot, joining her at the counter, pressing my arm to hers.

'I want to help.'

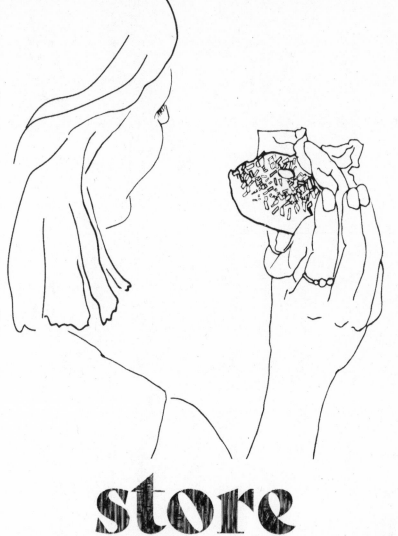

store
cupboard

The food that made you

EATING
BY HAND

SYEDA SALMAH

Perhaps you have noticed us before? Those of us with tandoori-stained fingers, or with a faint ochre stain left over from our mother's fried fish with onion masala, and especially those who have dipped into red chilli sauces and pickles to adorn our dishes with. On the outside, growing up at school, we were mocked for our 'curry fingers', but on the inside, amongst our community, we knew that it was all worth it. There is nothing better than the joy that comes with eating by hand.

Some of my fondest memories of my stern, disapproving mother are of when we have all gathered on the sitting room floor together by the sofa. Amma has come from the kitchen with a steaming plate of chicken curry with potatoes and we are silent with expectation. She artfully folds over hot, delicate pearls of rice with the curry and expertly tears off soft chunks of chicken. She does all this with the tips of her elegant and precise fingers, scoops it up deftly, and we await like chicks on a branch for a golden mouthful to be placed on our tongues.

This is normal. This is what happened growing up all the time – ask any Bengali person and they will smile nostalgically. For a brief moment, a family of seven in a crowded two-bedroom flat with peeling wallpaper was able to take a break from their chaotic lives and be joined together.

Much later, even as grown women, my cousins and I would love being babied by our youngest aunt, who was only a few years older than me, in her thirties. She was still waiting to get pregnant and she adored us. We would squeal, whilst perched on the edge of the sofa bed, and claim that she had given the best part of the lamb to the other, or no, no, no this mouthful was too big, Khala, I'm going to get so fat, and someone would be taking selfies the whole time. Now she has two wonderful babies of her own but if she were to offer me another mouthful I would jump at the chance, even at the age of thirty-three.

We all eat with our hands. If you truly love food, you will find it hard to deny the joy of gnawing away at the corner of a lamb chop or descending into a bag of salt-and-vinegar crisps; of scoffing down a handful of McDonald's fries whilst driving; of peeling a fragrant satsuma, or holding a perfectly buttered crumpet to your lips, or gently tearing meat away from the bone of smoked ribs. In those moments where we use our hands, those gifts from the Gods, we are joined in our appreciation of texture, fullness and anticipation.

At nearly every establishment I have had the pleasure of working at, I've also had the displeasure of being asked 'Why? Don't you know how to use cutlery?' when I reveal that my family eats with their hands. My revelation frequently evokes a voice full of pity, sometimes of mockery and often ignorance. Yes, of course I know how. Why would one method cancel out the other?

With every exchange of this kind, I have felt stupid for letting myself be exposed. Without realising it, that schoolgirl in me who was embarrassed of her curry fingers comes rushing through and I find myself stumbling a little in my response. Not because I do not have anything to say, but because I have so much to say. I have so much to show and teach these people.

It's not as easy as it looks, eating with your hands. It is an art unto itself and takes a few weeks of practice before you get it right. You begin with cleaning your hands, conscious that you are about to take part in a thousand-year ritual, as many others around the world do the same. You fold up your sleeves (turmeric is a whole colour filter of its own), grab your plate and let your eyes scan the table where all the dishes are presented. Then, with a spoon (because we don't actually harbour any hate towards utensils), you dig in and ladle up whatever sings to your heart. You might place this plate on your lap; maybe you're fancy, and your family sit at the table; or perhaps it's Ramadan, and with humility and grace you fold your legs and place it on the floor. And then you begin – blow carefully, it can be hot. With the tips of all your fingers, through plump, fluffy rice, you take a morsel of the softest piece of lamb torn from the bone and mix the juices through, composing a perfectly rounded handful. Then, using your thumbs, you scoop it into your mouth.

I've often wondered how people eat fish with knives and forks; it sounds near to impossible to enjoy the true taste of the white flakes of tamarind-soaked fish with a cold, glinting piece of metal. Forks were made for piercing, not blending flavours together. Eating by hand is an emotional and intimate experience that, once perfected, can make other forms of cutlery and silver service look like weapons in comparison.

The history of eating by hand goes back a long way – to the very same civilisations that our literature, architecture and elements of democracy are inspired by. Why not be inspired by their methods of eating, too?

Ayuverdic teaching, harking back nearly 3,000 years, emphasises that the very act of eating with our fingertips helps to support our digestive system. By interacting with food, we can manage our eating portions and our body is able to break down the natural and necessary good bacteria that our system needs to help maintain a healthy immune system. For these homeopathic philosophers with natural methods the hand with its five fingers represents all five elements of the universe.

When I first took my partner home with me – mostly because I needed to borrow Amma's rice cooker (a must in every household) – she was in a panic: what would she serve him? What would a lovely, Caucasian, English gentleman from the countryside like to eat at a traditional Bengali household in east London?

Shemai and puri, obviously.

He loved it. Digging in with both hands, eternally grateful and enjoying the different textures, he tore the crisp puri to help scoop the soft, milky vermicelli pudding. Until Abba, who sat across him, looked up at me and said in Bangla, 'Tell Jo to stop eating with his left hand.' I was mildly mortified and had to whisper to Jo as he slowed down and sheepishly attempted to use his right hand.

The rituals of eating by hand are manyfold. Bengali people only eat with their right – sometimes at the expense of lefties. The right hand is there to remind us of our conscious choices and the agency that we have to implement the foundations of our morals. You might write words of wisdom, care for your elders and feed others and yourself with it. The left hand isn't defunct, but the right hand serves as a concept, much like that of Midas's own gold hand, to bring us humility.

These days, Amma brings out a sixteen-piece cutlery set that no one uses to placate any future moments like this and it makes us all laugh. Jo never needs it, preferring to take part in the softer and informal approach of using his hands.

There are other rituals, especially during auspicious events, Eid celebrations and weddings where we all gather together to construct the most beautiful of dishes. A large taal, a silver steel dish that could feed three or four families, is placed in the centre of the room and artistic tasks are assigned. Here is Abba transforming a simple beef tomato into a lotus shaped flower; here is Mama carving symbols into a watermelon; and here is Mami delicately placing it all together. We become architects in the space of an evening and eventually form a grand display of rice, chicken, vegetable, eggs and, at other times fruits into a sculpture worthy of its own exhibition at Tate Modern. This is gently transported to the hall and presented in front of the groom, who then invites his friends, brothers and in-laws to gather around him and each reach out with their right hand to joyfully attack the sculpture, searching for the best bits of the roast chicken, laughing with delight. On another occasion, the bride and groom are presented with a gilded bowl full of pure white milk. She dips her hands in, as does he, and together they search for the wedding ring. It is said that whoever finds it first will be the one to lead, and often it's the bride.

These are communal and shared experiences. To eat by hand is to belong; to be part of something. The UK is a country made up of diverse ethnic backgrounds, enriched by the food and the customs of other cultures. And yet I grew up under the gaze of many people who thought I wasn't civilised enough because of the way I ate.

Where does this image of the barbarian come from? From where I stand, we have the East Asian community navigating through chopsticks, the Middle East and many countries that make up the African continent tackling food with unleavened bread, the Latin community devouring barbacoa with their corn-based starches and, finally, us South Asians, persistent with our fingers.

That leaves very few countries who don't employ their hands. Those very same countries also have a history of invading and conquering other vulnerable communities for their own purpose. The term 'barbarian' during the period of empire-building would have benefited a country who desperately needed a reason to justify colonising and enslaving another. There seems to be a direct correlation between assumptions that eating by hand is a form of savagery, and an imperial narrative that relies on destroying any form of humanity in a community that they intend to pillage.

It took me a while to learn how to navigate the world of knives and forks. I would watch shows on TV trying to imitate them. Sometimes, if I was lucky, there would be a scene where one of the characters would be as clueless as me and need instruction. What on earth was a soup spoon? What was soup? It looked like a bland version of dahl. Once, when I was ten years old and on a school residential trip to Gorsefield, I was asked to set the table. I was terrified. Who would I ask for help? The teachers looked exhausted and the other girl was named Eliza – I assumed she probably already knew what to do. So, I held back, hovered by the door and watched her until one of the cooks caught me and accused me of being lazy. To this day, I still identify with the archetypal 'dumb' character who manages to find themselves at a lavish dinner and is confounded by the endless number of forks on the table. I haven't perfected it and sometimes I give up halfway, choosing to pick at my food with my fingers.

What's changed is my confidence and sense of pride. Eating by hand is who I am. It's my culture, and I have spent too long being ashamed in lieu of others' ignorance. If I have paid an extortionate amount for a restaurant experience, by god I plan to enjoy myself without judgement.

But that pride can sometimes morph itself into something else. I have a cousin who married a kind and softly spoken gentleman, as arranged by her family, and with whom she now has two beautiful children in a home out in the countryside. When I heard he was from London, I figured he would be a good choice, assuming he would 'keep it real'. That was true enough, until Amma hosted a dinner, as is custom when introducing a newly married couple to the family, and he asked for a knife and fork. We all went quiet and many eyes darted over to me, the matriarchal elder sister that I am. I held back a snigger whilst my mum ran off to bring that same sixteen-piece set she always saves for Jo.

It turned out the new groom never eats with his hand. It was one thing to be mocked by an outsider, but here, by my very own cousin's husband? Surely not. Did he think he was better than us? Had he too been a victim of curry fingers and had that manifested itself into a dislike and refusal to eat with his hand? Or was he simply averse to it and completely entitled to his own opinion and experience?

Throughout my life, and perhaps that of many other Bengalis growing up in a Western-centric world, there remains an undertone of being two people, two minds; of cutlery and the right hand, constantly at battle with each other, struggling for pride and space.

For me, exercising this method of eating in its traditional format remains a way to not only express my culture but also to flagrantly demonstrate that Britain has always been and will always be a country with a multicultural history. One way of reminding people of this who might think otherwise is to show my hand. To expose myself to the possible disdain, and literally and figuratively reach out.

APRIKOSEN, MARILLEN

MARIA ILONA MOORE

I'm not sure what spreads and jams were the staples in other kitchens in the small town I grew up in, but in our house there was always apricot jam. Not just any apricot jam, but homemade-by-my-German-grandmother-and-brought-over-in-her-suitcase jam. And not that stodgy, gelatinous type of jam either – this was the kind that was sometimes more like a compote when you opened the lid. We had jars and jars at home at all times. I have a vague memory that when we moved house there was even a box that was just full of jars of apricot jam; it definitely felt that way, anyway. I've never found a similar version in the UK, though I've also never looked for one because I know it won't compare. Sometimes I've scrambled eagerly to open a jar of apricot jam on someone else's table (it's rare, and more likely to be found in one of those tiny packets you get at a Travelodge breakfast buffet) but I've always been thoroughly disappointed by the smooth pale jelly inside, which tastes more of sugar than anything else. It's nothing like my family's kind of apricot jam, which is rich and deep in flavour, and leaves behind a sticky orange stain when it drips off your slice of toast and lands in a dollop on the front of your T-shirt.

I can't speak German, not really, but I can understand it fluently and have always felt like the language is embedded deep inside me somewhere. My mum gave up speaking German to me because I'd just stubbornly reply in English, but it's still a part of me, inherently, learnt mostly by osmosis back when I was a child listening to the conversations of adults. Occasionally it pops up from the depths of my memory, unexpected, unannounced, but very welcome. Sometimes this comes in my dreams – the ones where I can speak fluently and wake up sorely disappointed – but more often it is in the words that come to me instinctually. I hear *Vorsicht* in my head before I hear *careful* or *watch out*, perhaps because I heard the German warning more when I was growing up, when I was still learning how to be *vorsichtig*. Other times, it's more like when you get a song stuck in your head, a word or phrase plays over and over in my mind for seemingly no reason. There is a joke I think about a lot, also jam-related, about a frog (a Breitmaulfrosch) saying *Marmelade* and *Confiture*. There is my grandma's sing-songy morning greeting, *Guten Morgen, Ohne Sorgen*, which I feel the urge to say when my friends stay over and we rise sleepily together, feeling totally at home with each other. And then there is *Aprikosen und Marillen*.

In the German I know, the German my family speaks, an apricot is an *Aprikose*, but in Austria, where my grandmother lives and where I spent my summers as a child, the word is *Marille*. It used to confuse me, the differences between the two variations of the language. I was anxious enough about getting it wrong, so suddenly finding out there were different words for the same thing only added to that. *Aprikose* made sense for obvious reasons; *Marille* felt like something flouncy, something extra to remember. But now this duality has become a comfort. I think of both words when the fruit is in season and the punnets are stacked up in Lidl, just like I can't walk past the ketchup aisle without hearing Mr Burns's 'ketchup/catsup' refrain from *The Simpsons*. It would seem apricots have become inadvertently embedded in my personal history.

Apricots are underrated. Everyone knows peaches and nectarines, but the humble apricot is often left out. Sometimes even I forget it – my mind flits to the hot-pink refreshment of the watermelon, the sangria-red playfulness of the cherry, the everyday ease of a crisp Granny Smith – and it's not until I see them return to the supermarket sometime around May that I remember how much I love them. But when I take the pack home, rip the plastic netting from the box and dig in, I'm disappointed. I was over-eager and didn't want to wait for it to ripen, so it's hard and tart, the inside more the watercolour of a cantaloupe than the poster-paint orange I'm used to. I try another and get the same result. Then another and this time, it's almost there, the flesh giving way easily in my palms, but the taste still lacking the depth I'm used to.

The perfect apricot you can pull apart with your thumbs into two perfect halves. It is a rich glowing orange, the colour of a jar of marmalade in the sun or a brand new traffic cone, one that hasn't been weather-worn and faded yet. It is juicy, but doesn't drip everywhere like when you bite into a peach or an overripe pear; it's thicker, more syrupy. And the taste is a rich mix of sweet and tart and floral; not as soapy as a Parma Violet though, don't worry.

Maybe the apricot is underrated because we just don't get good ones in the UK, or at least not in my local supermarket. Because when I tuck into a perfectly ripe apricot in my grandmother's kitchen, I sometimes think I've never tasted anything so good.

It wasn't just apricot jam and the actual fruits I ate at my grandma's, there was cake and biscuits too. The biscuits were tiny folds of sweet buttery pastry with apricot jam. The corners of the pastry wrap round the filling like it's giving it a hug. These would be on a tray with other delicate cookies, dusted in icing sugar (*Puderzucker*) and with various fillings – but the apricot ones were always my favourite. The cake my grandmother made herself: a simple, flat, square spongey base with apricot halves pressed into it. It could be frozen to make it more manageable to get through (as if I needed help) and I remember taking slabs back to England with me, tied up in a blue freezer bag to help it survive the journey. It never tasted quite the same when I got off the plane. I asked for the recipe once, eager to make it when I returned to my own kitchen, and she wrote it out by hand for me on a sheet of notepaper from the pad she keeps by the telephone. But, of course, I didn't bake it once I got back. I don't really bake, and I wouldn't be able to find any good apricots anyway.

It turns out the subpar apricots found in the Lidl down the road are, most likely, actually rubbish – not just rubbish because they don't compare to my nostalgic, sun-drenched, rose-tinted version. Apricots are a fragile fruit, needing a stable climate and an early summer (I mean, who doesn't?). They tend to get picked and shipped before they're ripe, so they're easier to transport and ready and uniform for the eager supermarket shopper. That's why in the UK we so often end up with what Hugh Fearnley-Whittingstall refers to as a 'woolly, watery disappointment'. Despite this pallid reality, I still hope for John Ruskin's more flattering description of apricots, 'shining in a sweet brightness of golden velvet', when I see them in the shop.

I live my life through cultural references, and I can't help but feel the apricot needs its day in the sun. The peach got its happy ending in *Call Me By Your Name*; the plum, 'so sweet, and so cold', as William Carlos Williams put it, has become a well-versed meme; the apple is, of course, everywhere. There is the heavy symbolism of the pomegranate and the romantic side of strawberries, that chocolate-covered stalwart of Valentine's desserts. But what about my dear apricot? To me, it is a fruit of dualities and dichotomies. It is Aprikose, it is Marille. It is the bland, chilled supermarket variety and the luxurious sun-warmed softness of the ones I know from my childhood. It is sweet and delicate; intense, yet unpretentious. It is not as sexy as a peach, but it has that same connotation in the ripeness of its flesh, the shape of the fruit, the vibrancy of its shade. It is so familiar to me, intertwined with my family's history, which is as convoluted as anyone's, intrinsically European, both close and just out of reach. Yet with that familiarity comes expectations that can't quite be met. I think I'm learning to accept the contradictions, to sit with the difference.

I may never find the perfect apricot outside of my summers in Austria, but one thing I can be sure of is the fruit will always be a comfort, so tied up with the nostalgia of the jam and the biscuits and the cake I'll never bake.

DAD IS DEAD MOM SOLD THE CHICKENS

PAULA HILTON

Between my thumb
and forefinger, the last
brown egg. My warmth
seeps into its cold shell.
Sweat beads appear on egg's
face. Dad is nine days gone.

I apply pressure. Not enough
to break. Not enough to touch
life's messy unevenness or to
understand fragile boundaries.
How would it feel to let this last
of Dad slide through my fingers?

Instead, I choose a practicality
he'd admire. Cracking the egg
on a hot skillet's side, I scramble
white and yolk together with a fork.
As liquid takes shape, I see my hands
dicing a slice of ripe tomato, a little
green pepper, some fragrant onion,
all picked from our garden.

I wonder at my fingers moving briskly,
mocking in their cheerfulness as they
scatter vegetables on top of Dad's egg.
Finished, the spatula in my hand places
this new creation onto a cool, white plate.

A door opens. My three-year-old daughter
bounds from her room, eyes bright, mind
uncomplicated by grief. I place the dish
before her at the breakfast table. 'It's pretty,
Mommy,' she says. Then, I watch as she's
nourished by the last of Dad's eggs, this
granddaughter who looks like him.

meals for one

What food means to you

PRISON
CAKE

CANDY IKWUWUNNA

People generally know the deal when they're past this point of the journey. Still, Uzoma shifts the cake tin – housing a sloppily iced carrot cake – onto the seat beside him and covers it with his jacket. He isn't trying to get any *more* looks on the bus to Her Majesty's Prison Thameside. At least, no more than usual.

Obi talked about the food on their last call. He had never had the best digestive system, one of the few things Uzoma doesn't miss about him. He was laughing, half mirth, half disbelief, as he spoke about the wet pizza, the soggy chips, the salty Friday-night curries, the small sachets of cereal that left him hungry, stomach growling by mid-morning.

Uzo could hear it in his voice, despite Obi's best efforts. When they spoke on the buzzy phone line, they both tried to keep their tones light, never far off a joke or a funny story. But sometimes on their weekly calls, it felt like they were kids again, like he was hopping over broken pavements, convinced that if he stepped down too hard on a crack, they would both fall into darkness. Uzo wasn't sure how to say to his younger brother that he didn't have to be ashamed of needing more.

Still, it's Obi's birthday, and Uzo spent the best part of last night making a carrot cake, Obi's favourite. For Uzo, cooking is a means to an end, and his baking skills are near non-existent. The sponges feel a bit soft, and the batter, stuffed with carrot and ginger shavings, walnuts and rum, was a bit spicy, but it doesn't look too bad, and the icing is tangy and sweet. He hopes Obi loves it.

In the end, they don't let him in with the cake. The prison warden watches Uzo as he stutters and cajoles, but he is a brick wall of will, or at least one used to the stone throws of the wheedles of loved ones who misread the rules.

Obi laughs when Uzo tells him the cake is resting in a box in the waiting room. 'Uzo, oh my god, you're so embarrassing, man. I hope they're not too mad. I'm not trying to fall out of favour with any of the staff.'

'I don't know what they thought I was bringing in,' Uzo protests. 'Maybe next time I'll try hiding the bolt cutters in my boxers.'

Obi shushes him, eyeing one of the guards at the side of the visiting room. 'Probably drugs. And don't even joke about it, they're always listening to the stuff we say. I don't want any privileges taken away.'

Obi is still smiling, but it's tight, like someone has hooked the edges of his mouth. Uzoma wonders how someone can look younger and older at the same time. Obi has grown out his beard, his hair thick and puffy on top of his head. Lines have etched onto his face, too many for a twenty-two-year-old, and his hands sit in fists on the table. Uzo knows this means Obi is hiding the tremors he sometimes gets when he's anxious or angry. Uzoma spots the very slight discolouring on his face, the fading of a bruise.

The carrot cake is heavy on his lap the whole bus ride home. When he gets back to his flat, he eats a slice, then another, then another, then another, until it tastes like mud on his tongue, and he throws the rest away. He feels the shame and guilt curdle in his stomach. He wants to crawl out of his skin. He wishes he could shed his old self, his old life, like it's a ratty coat, step into a new one where he can be there for his brother.

The wind whistles on his street. He can hear the roar of the DLR, making its way to central London. The house is silent save for his breathing.

It's nights like this when he misses them all the most. Misses the mum who held his hand while he skipped over those cracked pavements. Misses the little brother that followed him around. Misses Ezra, who kissed him like he was always so sure about them. The ache of them gone hurts like a blade. It rises like dust in an old room, and no matter where he turns, how he moves, it gets buried in his throat, and he can't help but choke.

At his annual appraisal, Uzo's boss told him he needs to be more sociable. 'People like you, Uzo, but they'd like to see more of you,' Eric said, squeezing his hands together on the table in his office, his face earnest. Eric mentioned it after going through Uzo's official objectives, so he knows that, no matter what he does in the next year, being social is what he needs to tie the bow on the package of his accomplishments if he wants to advance. Uzoma wanted to retort back that he'd be more social if someone had said something in response to Jeffrey's stupid 'stick a lion on it' joke at the African markets presentation run-through, instead of the wet tepid laughs it had received instead.

He'd gone back to his desk after that meeting feeling like he had swallowed a rock on fire that was burning him from the inside. He ate a Rich Tea from the biscuit tin Christine kept for their department. He had another, then moved to another workstation to keep himself from another binge, his body brittle for the rest of the day.

He didn't really know how to tell Eric that, these days, his energy was drained to the dregs by the evening. He had tried when he came to the company as a new graduate. He went to all the parties, barbecues, pub quizzes, sponsored runs and team-building weekends. And they were fun, until they weren't. Until Obi's arrest, when it felt like an invisible partition sprung up between him and his colleagues. Suddenly the jests about Uzo scoring them weed or the quips about fraudster Nigerian princes or the gay jokes didn't slide so easily off him, and he was beginning to think they never had. He no longer knew how to fold parts of himself away so that they could be comfortable. Someone relaxing around him enough to let the cap off their filter while his was still drilled on wasn't the reward he once thought it was. It felt easier to retreat.

Still. He was trying to make Senior Analyst by the time Obi got out, so he smiled back at Eric and nodded and agreed, then signed up to the book club he saw on the company intranet. He is in the canteen one day, flicking through *Normal People* by Sally Rooney, when he hears the scrape of a chair being pulled to his table. He looks up and sees Ezra taking a seat across from him.

'Why do you have carrots in your lunch if you hate them?' Ezra asks.

He's in his running gear, which means that he has come back from his lunchtime jog. He starts to lay out his food. Ezra always brings the kind of lunch that is near enough a celebratory feast. His Tupperware contains what looks like heated up oxtail stew and rice, with a heaped salad in another section, bursting with the colours of chopped beetroot and tomatoes, shavings of cucumber, lettuce and even Uzo's dreaded carrots. He also brings out chocolate chip granola bars that Uzo knows Ezra makes at home every Sunday, that he keeps in his locker to eat as snacks during the week.

Not that Uzo has noticed anything about Ezra. Not that he is still thinking about him.

Uzo scowls. His lunch was a salad with beef chunks, the marinade spread unevenly over the packet instant rice. The unevenly chopped carrot chunks remain in his bowl. 'This is the kind of judgement I get for trying to be healthy.'

Ezra smiles. 'I wasn't talking about – I mean, I just think you should enjoy your food, Uzo.'

Ezra never has lunch at his desk. Mealtimes for Ezra are treasures, little goldmines during the day. Hours to breathe, to spend time with the food he likes, and people he loves, if he can help it.

Uzo ignores how hearing his name in Ezra's teasing tone makes his stomach flutter. He brings one of the carrot pieces to his mouth. It tastes like dirt, but he finishes it. 'See? That was great.'

'Here.' Ezra elbows him his container of granola bars. 'Have one of these.'

Uzo picks up another carrot piece. 'No, honestly, these taste great. I'm enjoying myself.'

Ezra chuckles, and shakes his head a little. 'You're really not as good at hiding your feelings as you think you are.'

*

He couldn't really pinpoint when the thing with Ezra started. He was just in it, one day, seeing him everywhere he turned, unable to stop the growing snowball of his feelings. He remembers Ezra being new to the company, his face and his easy smile and the vision of him in his running gear causing a small quake through the office. But Uzo didn't speak to him much at first, apart from the obligatory nod and hello in meetings.

But then they were put on an emerging-markets project together, and suddenly they were staying late in the office, long after they had to, talking until Uzo's voice was hoarse. The project finished, but they met up again and again, for lunch, for drinks after work, to go to plays and the cinema. It felt like the first time Uzo didn't temper his thoughts before they left his mouth. They would speak for hours, about Ezra's love of cooking shows, even though he knew he wasn't precise enough for them, and Uzo's summer of skateboarding to impress a guy he liked. Ezra's childhood running around in Falmouth, in Jamaica, and how he cried almost every night for a year when they moved to Croydon the winter he turned seven. Ezra's hikes in Epping Forest, his love of the big sprawling outdoor spaces, despite his insistence he could never leave London now. Their favourite movies (Ezra loved ones with endings that would leave them arguing by text message into the night; Uzo liked some fun, some romance, and then carrying on with his evening). It was, Uzo realised one morning as they made plans over email to try out a new Mexican restaurant at lunch, nice to have a friend at work. And that's all it was, he lectured himself. He collected crushes like mini fairy cakes at a bake sale, icing sugary on his tongue, their sweetness getting him through the day. But apart from a few situationships over the years, they rarely led to anything more. He didn't know how to speak the language of not being alone.

But Ezra felt different. Ezra didn't hold back his opinions when he was around Uzo and Uzo didn't hold back his. He remembers that winter morning, when he was at the top of the stairs carrying half a croissant breakfast, when he tried to open the door to the office and got stuck in a tangle of headphones, hair, bag straps and jacket zips, his music still blaring. In the chaos, he felt steady hands on him, carefully spinning him round, looping out the wires, moving his bag strap out the way. Ezra dusted the flakes of the almond croissant off his face, his thumb lingering, touching Uzo like he was a precious thing. Ezra had been laughing, but he'd stopped, his face unreadable as the air between them heated, as charged as a current.

'As you can see, I was getting there,' Uzo said, the words so weak in the moment that they fell between them, useless.

Ezra just nodded, then shook his head, as if he remembered where they were. As he walked away, holding the door open, Uzo felt something blooming in him, faster than he could control. He could hear SWV still singing in his ears. *Yikes yikes yikes* he thought. *Yes. Yes. Yes.*

They went back to Ezra's the night of the Christmas party. Uzo almost wishes he didn't, so he didn't replay it so much in his head. Ezra's hands everywhere on him; Uzo not thinking about his body except to be surprised that it had so much pleasure stored in it, waiting to be teased out. He slept in Ezra's jumper, gathered in his arms.

In the morning, Ezra made omelettes stuffed with peppers and spinach, their faces as hot as the frying oil. They couldn't stop smiling at each other.

Out of the two of them, Obi was the far superior cook, even better than their mum. For all she had fretted about him, he was rapt when it was just them and her in the kitchen together. In the run up to Obi's sentencing, he cooked almost every day. Uzo would come home to find chicken with herbs rubbed into the flesh, marinating on the sink. There would be pepper soup with gizzard and shaki sitting on the stove, so hot it burned his mouth and he had to chase it down with milk. Vegetable soup with spinach and grilled mushrooms, served with eba or pounded yam. Palm oil stew with catfish fillets, brown rice and fried plantain, crisp and cubed, on the side. It was so much that Uzo almost couldn't remember a time when he didn't come home to the little kitchen windows sweating.

Neither of them was eating or sleeping that much. The uncertainty and worry about what was coming was a heavy weight on their chests. But it beat other periods of time in their flat. Times when it was normal to be sent to bed without dinner for talking back, his stomach groaning and growling like it was a living thing. Nights when their mum didn't manage to sneak them in some snacks. When they would put headphones in to drown out the arguments. Times when their dad would storm and shout. Times when he did more than that.

On the last day, Obi tried to make plantain and banana bread, until Uzo told him to breathe, to take a nap. Uzo could see Obi's hands were trembling, his voice shaking, his concentration lapsing. Obi was like a brewing stock pot of feeling, and he hated to disappoint. Shame and anger could burn him, in a way that got him into fights, suspended and expelled, in and out of learning centres and schools, police cars driving him home to their father's wrath, at least until he died. Uzo never knew what to say to the boy shivering in his bed, his eyes red rimmed, not knowing what to do with the storm inside him that could so easily turn into a weapon.

'It's probably better I didn't finish it anyway, I was gonna make it with Nutella and we don't have any,' Obi said, stirring the batter once more before they left for court, his tag blinking around his ankle.

'You can finish it when we get home,' Uzoma said.

Obi didn't say anything.

Once the judge gave Obi three years, Uzo returned home alone. He eyed the fridge, brimming with leftovers, and sat down in a ball, shutting his eyes tight, as if he could squeeze out thoughts of Obi's face in the dock, his hands shackled as they led him back to his cell.

He eyed the fridge much later, everything in it feeling like a bomb about to go off. He knew Obi had made all this for him, to look after himself in the first few weeks when he was gone. But all Uzo knew how to do was to eat until it hurt. All that love, tucked away in Tupperware, pots, bowls with cling film and foil rolled over the top. All that comfort, that Uzo knew could turn so easily into a weapon.

He's glad things have thawed between him and Ezra. They had a couple of weeks where Uzo kept his panic at bay, but it caught up to him eventually, clawing up his throat every time Ezra would ask about Uzo's family, his friends, his parents. He could tell Ezra was puzzled by the vague answers.

Ezra talked to his mum and dad every day, but Uzo knew his life, his family, wasn't perfect. He knew Ezra ran at lunch more for his head than he did his body. He knew he missed his grandparents back in Jamaica desperately. He knew that some of Ezra's uncles and aunts still had something to say about him liking men as well as women. He knew, in theory, that nobody's life was perfect. But still, Uzo didn't know how he would explain everything to Ezra – Obi; his parents, so different, both gone; his eating. He didn't know how to pull out one weed, without being scared of all the bodies he could exhume. When they were briefly dating, Uzo noticed that Ezra tried to enjoy his life, make his days and weeks something to feast on, as much as he could. Uzo didn't know what to make of that. His days felt like cheese gone damp and mouldy, forgotten at the back of the fridge.

It seemed easier, a few days after Christmas, to text *I think we should just be friends.*

He knows he has no right to still want Ezra. He hurt him, after all, and he has to live with that, let him move on. Ezra is still friendly, always smiling, but no more than that after the Christmas break. No chat messages, no emails outside of actual work issues, no lunch invitations, no invitations to anything at all. Seeing him around the office feels like Uzo ate one bite of a gooey cookie before the rest of it crumbled to the floor. He has no business trying to piece it back together.

One Sunday, Uzo decides to take a walk through his area instead of wilting in his flat, worrying about Obi. He passes endless streets of houses with people sitting in their front yards, enjoying the sunshine of early summer, kids spraying each other with water guns. He hears music blaring out of cars and garden speakers, the sounds of laughter, of families breaking bread together for Sunday lunch, of churches finishing service with big numbers led by their choirs. There is something about it all that loosens him.

He ends up walking up close to Deptford town centre, further than he means to, passing the new vegan bakeries, the little breweries, the craft beer pubs and restaurants with queues out the door, the bric-a-brac stalls. He wanders around until he happens on a little stand selling everything from chin-chin, to bofrot, to dry crayfish in packs, to spinach for vegetable soup, to garden eggs and alligator pepper. He sees a crate of plantains, '4 for £1'.

'I'll take eight,' he finds himself saying.

The woman commandeering the stall nods and gestures. 'Sure, pick the ones you want.'

He picks them up, a mixture of green ones with their skins probably still glued to the flesh, not ready to be peeled, to the browning one that is a couple of days away from being thrown out.

She packs it all up for him. He smiles at her before leaving, noticing Igbo gospel playing on her speakers, the lilt of her accent. He starts to leave and then turns back.

'*Imela*,' he says, the word clunky out of his mouth. 'Have a good day.'

She chuckles, it's unexpected. '*Odinma* my dear,' she says. 'Enjoy your Sunday.'

He picks up some Nutella and bananas on the way back. When he's home, he mashes the plantain, banana, eggs, butter, sugar, flour and Nutella into a batter, soft and giving, and watches it rise in the oven over the late afternoon hour.

It is hot when he tastes it, still crumbly. But it's sweet, and creamy. Obi would love it.

He wraps up the rest and sits at his table. At Christmas, after Ezra, the loneliness had been eating at his heart like a worm. He had binged through the day, not actually tasting the food he prepared, not knowing how to stop. Suddenly he saw his whole life sprawl out in front of him, his hands and his heart too busy wrestling with this to give themselves to anything else.

He had started an email to an eating disorder therapist. He finishes it now, the whoosh of it going the only sound in his flat.

*

As he waits to be connected to Obi for their weekly phone call, Uzo is wondering whether to tell Obi about his first few sessions, strange and awkward as they've been. Then the phone line clicks and Obi is talking, running out his words before Uzo can make sense of them.

'Wait, wait, hang on,' Uzo says, his heart ticking up. 'What's going on?'

Obi takes a deep, jittering breath to say his news. He got a delivery of documents this morning. Documents detailing that the release date of one Amobi Kenneth Ofor had been brought forward to a date only one month away.

'I'm coming home,' he's saying, like he doesn't quite believe it. 'I'm coming home.'

'Yes, you are,' Uzo says. 'I can't—' but his voice is growing thicker with tears as each word comes out, so he stops.

'Will you come pick me up?' Obi starts to ask, but Uzo doesn't let him finish. Of course he will. Of course he will.

Uzo feels restless, like he is slightly out of his body for the next week. His heart feels like it wants to float out of him. His hands shake after he's had his morning coffee.

'Come back to your body,' Max, his therapist, always tells him. 'What is it telling you?'

He does his breathing exercises in the stairwell, his ambient beats playlist in his ears. He tries to sit down and really eat his food, chewing slowly, tasting every single thing his hands have molded together in his little kitchen. He tries to take his walks, he tries to record his thoughts, he's trying to learn what caring for himself means.

He goes on a walk one lunchtime in Temple Gardens, when he sees Ezra on a bench, a crumpled-up sandwich pack beside him. The bench is in front of a rosebush, and Ezra's head is tilted back, eyes covered by his sunglasses. He looks like he is soaking up the sun. He looks like a painting.

Uzo feels his heart contract. All that effort, all that time, trying to stay away from the edge of a cliff. In the end, he had fallen anyway. And hurt someone gentle and tender, to boot.

His legs start moving before he gives them permission, and then he is in front of him, Ezra's deep brown eyes widening, a hint of a tentative smile on his face.

'You okay?' Ezra asks softly.

Now that he is in front of him, Uzo feels like he is about to pass out. He feels like he wants to run away. But he owes Ezra this. And he wants him. He knows it's unfair to want, to expect anything at all, but here he is still.

'Can we talk?' Uzo says.

The night before Obi gets out, Uzo prepares.

He grinds up tomatoes, fresh from Ezra's vines, for the jollof. He sautés garlic, scallions and scotch bonnet peppers, before adding the flakes of saltfish and ackee straight from the can until the pan is smoky and hissing. He skewers grilled meats, covered in yaji, with peeled purple onion slices. He dices vegetables for the salad, chopping with so much vigour that half the cucumber ends up on the floor. He bakes the plantain, banana and Nutella cake, then makes up a traybake to cool overnight, the crystallised ginger gems winking from the chocolatey mixture.

He collapses on the sofa later that night, sweat cooling on his forehead. He thinks about the many evenings he could have now, him and Obi and maybe Ezra, sitting at their dining table, eating together, over time, the smells and scents of their cooking sinking between the walls. All the meals they could make, open, food warm in his hands, rather than secret, ashamed, burning his heart.

He looks at all the mismatched meals littering his kitchen. Obi will love it. He's coming home now. He deserves a feast.

And – Uzo realises, as he jumps up and spoons some jollof onto a plate – so does he.

A CRAB
FOR ONE

KATE YOUNG

One night, a couple of weeks before my twenty-eighth birthday, I eschewed post-work Friday night drinks in favour of returning home early. There was a promising evening ahead – rounds had been suggested, bowls of chips mooted, the tantalising promise of the best late-night kebabs Kilburn High Road had to offer once we finally called it a night. But I had an early start; my alarm was set for 3.30 a.m. and I needed to be in bed by nine. I wasn't heading to an airport, didn't need to be up for work, wasn't heading off on a day-long adventure. It was, in fact, all in pursuit of a crab for lunch. Not one to serve at a dinner party, you understand, or for a partner or dear friend. It was a crab just for me.

I avoided the inevitable temptation to snooze my alarm in the dark the next morning, got on the first early morning bus to London's Docklands, and navigated the strange industrial estates and over- and underpasses that surround Billingsgate Fish Market.

I found a bucket of brown crabs, had a conversation with the woman next to me about recognising a good one (she should feel heavy for her size, apparently), ate a bacon-and-scallop roll and drank a strong cup of tea from an urn at the on-site caff, and returned home on the bus with the crab in a bag on the seat next to me. I spent the journey contemplating the advice I had read and watched on killing a crab, wondering how successfully I was going to be able to pull it off.

Oddly, this was somehow both exactly and nothing at all like what I had imagined my twenties would bring.

My relationship with food was cultivated and encouraged early on. We had a house filled with cookbooks, collected over the decades my mother had been cooking – her teenage years in Australia, her twenties in England, her thirties back where she had been raised. I read her books voraciously, remembering meals she'd made for us and for guests, suggesting ones we could try in the future, making notes on my favourites – the ones that drew me in with a photograph, a description, a beloved ingredient.

The first cookbook I owned myself was a weighty one. An encyclopaedia of desserts, it towered over the battered secondhand paperbacks on my bookshelves. Its pages were glossy and thick, the pictures throughout stark and bright and functional in that way that food photography often was in the 1990s. I bought it with the book vouchers I had won at school for my Year 9 results; before walking into the bookshop I had planned to spend them on a boxed collection of Shakespeare's plays and sonnets, but somehow found myself in the cookery section instead. Every year that followed, after I shook hands with our school principal and collected my vouchers and certificate, I ventured back to the culinary section of the bookshop, eager to grow my collection.

In these early years, when the food I was making and the time I was spending in the kitchen was at the behest of my parents, this small shelf of cookbooks became a portal into adulthood. I sat on my bed or on the back deck, immersing myself in lists of ingredients, in reassuring directions, in descriptions of meals I wanted to experience. I made plans for the dinner parties I would hold one day, for the food I would cook for my family, for the parts of the big Christmas dinner I would take on once I had a kitchen of my own. I wrote out menus in full, giving my school friends and me imaginary husbands that we'd share the table with. I assumed I would grow up to be the type of woman who took a guest back to the kitchen to chat with while I prepared *île flottante*, or blowtorched the sugar atop the *crème brûlée*, while my husband continued to charm our guests in the next room.

For a teenager who identified as a feminist, able to imagine myself in any number of jobs and rarely considering my gender a barrier to achieving anything, it feels odd looking back that my dream home-life played out in my head like a 1950s sitcom. I had career aspirations – at various points a paediatrician, a criminal barrister, an author, a theatre producer – but I imagined that my weekends would be filled with a sort of easy domesticity, with soccer matches and swim meets and play dates, and with food around a dining table. It was how I grew up; my mum worked hard through the week, and then hosted dinner parties and filled the freezer with meals we'd need down the line when the weekends arrived.

When I was young, all those relationships that were modelled in front of me, the ones I aspired to, were resoundingly heteronormative. There were some divorces, of course, but family life in inner-northwest Brisbane had a specific look to it: a marriage with a partner (a man, for me, obviously), and a collection of children.

I didn't even try to imagine any other sort of life because what I most deeply wanted was to be successful – to fit with the narrative I was presented. And so many of the women I admired – my mum, my granny, friends' mothers, Sookie on *Gilmore Girls* – showed their love and built their homes around food.

The food I wanted to cook in the future was *for* people; to welcome, to nourish, to comfort, to impress. Despite knowing just how much pleasure food brought me personally, there was an undeniable performativity to the role I imagined it would always play. The five hundred pages of desserts in that first cookbook weren't for me, they were for my family – my husband and children, down the line, but my parents and sister in the meantime. I bought it not because of what I wanted to eat, but because of what I wanted to cook and, most importantly, what I wanted to serve.

Despite my best-laid (obsessive, overwrought) plans, my thirties have not brought with them that image of my life that I assumed was in my future. There are multiple reasons for and manifestations of this: I moved to a different country and don't spend Christmas with my parents; I don't yet have children to cook for; I live on my own. And I'm gay. The fictional husband who shared my dining table started to look drastically less appealing this side of thirty, as I began to truly comprehend my sexuality.

I spent my first ten years in the UK in London, sharing a couple of rooms with an occasionally rotating cast of friends and strangers, inviting people over to eat dinner around the coffee table that sat at the centre of my small magnolia-painted flat. My impulse was still to create home and family where I could, to serve up meals for people I loved. I planned elaborate menus and tried new recipes. I rolled out tortillas and battered prawns for tacos, I made loaf after loaf of bread, I baked elaborate cakes for birthday parties and ordinary Tuesdays. I invited everyone back to mine at 3 a.m. after we'd spent the night dancing and made *croque monsieur* or pancakes or hastily thrown together noodles. I asked my mum to send photos of the desserts from that old book back home, too heavy to put in my backpack when I moved over.

But I also found an unanticipated joy in cooking for myself. I read Laurie Colwin's *Home Cooking*, and found an ally: a woman who looked forward to nights in alone, who would stop off for an aubergine and some red peppers and would make a solo dinner in her one-room apartment in Greenwich Village. In my teenage imaginings of my culinary future, I never dreamed that feeding myself would bring me so much pleasure. I started to make plans for it, for evenings 'off' when I knew I could have the flat to myself, writing lists and menus the way that I did when cooking for a crowd – except this time, I was cooking just for me.

I spent hours testing and proving dough to make a batch of (terrifically uninspiring, that first time) bao buns, filled with a tiny piece of pork I had cooked for the occasion. On paydays, I made a huge bowl of my favourite dish: *spaghette alla vongole*, enough, probably, for two, if I had cared to share. I didn't.

In that flat in Haggerston, some of the best meals I made were the ones I made for myself. Clams and steak and oysters are some of my favourite foods, but are undeniably expensive – beyond my budget when I considered making them for a big group. But for a single serving, I could just about justify it. It was worth saving up, or walking instead of getting on the Tube, in order to eat the thing I really wanted to eat. And so I started to make extravagant solo food plans. I rose at 3.30 a.m. and caught two buses across east London towards Billingsgate Fish Market in pursuit of that live crab that hissed in the seat next to me the whole way home. I had turned her into a salad by noon, those online videos useful in working out how to dispatch her, and had the rest of her – brown meat and white – on toast that evening.

In truth, it wasn't until years later, when I stopped photographing every meal I ate, that I was finally, truly, cooking just for me. There are only so many shots of eggs and crisp-fried greens and toast that anyone needs and, while my plans revolved around being able to take a well-lit, attractive photograph of whatever was on my plate, I was still seeking to feed others – to nourish them, and to impress them.

Living on my own for the first time, without supervision, without anyone else to feed – either physically or virtually – I focused instead on what I was eating. That continues to be a mixed bag: elaborately planned meals, seafood as often as I can get it, plenty of cheese on toast, bowls of dumplings from the supermarket that I store in a bag in the freezer and eat drowned in sticky chilli sauce, fried eggs and chips on cold nights, roughly chopped salads, a whole freezer-chilled cucumber when it's unbearably hot, soup made with the guilty ends of the vegetable drawer. I don't carve out time to eat alone anymore; I know I'll be doing it at least a couple of times a week. And so the pressure is off when it comes to making every one of those occasions perfect. I'm happy to pick whichever chair suits my mood: a tall stool in my kitchen, a corner of the sofa, the best side of the dining table (the one that affords me a view, of course). Like Madeleine Bourdouxhe's titular character in her novel *Marie*, a married woman in Paris who relishes her nights at home alone, my use of cutlery is functional rather than polite, I embrace the company of a book, and I exist in 'a delicious state of solitude'.

I feel a true, visceral joy at the prospect of a meal and an evening on my own terms.

I still love cooking for other people, for a big group of friends, for a girlfriend, for my surrogate family here and my beloved biological one when I visit Australia, for the children I used to nanny (and perhaps my own some day). I love long dinner parties that stretch out like our elastic waistbands as we open another bottle of wine. I love pulling a friend into the kitchen with me while I turn the top of the *crème brûlée* to hard caramel, as my guests entertain and charm each other around the table. I love lunches with all the windows thrust open, light dancing on the walls of the dining room as the afternoon marches on. I love hosting Christmas parties and Midsummer parties and birthday parties, and chatting away with the friends who stay to help wash up once everyone has gone home.

But so much of what I love about food are those specific details I really focus on when I'm eating alone: the taste of salted butter, and the way it seeps through toasted crumpets; the impulse and instinct and desire that kick in when you're dreaming up a menu; the soothing satisfaction of stirring a risotto slowly over a low heat; biting through the skin of a perfectly ripe apple; the flow of the seasons from one into the next and the ingredients that return to the market with reassuring consistency; the texture and savoury richness of a well-aged steak.

First, and foremost, it is food that I love. The chance to put it in front of others who may love it too is a bonus – I still want that family to cook for one day, though the picture looks different to how it once did. In the meantime, though, I am relishing those nights I spend alone, feet on the bar of the stool in my kitchen, book in hand, a single plate in front of me, offering up exactly what it is I want to eat.

HONEY CAKE

AMY FELDMAN

I

As summer fades into autumn, Grandma's freezer fills with portions of treacle-brown honey cake. The exact number changes each year – grandchildren moving out, starting their own homes; friends no longer with us – but there is always one for each household, and a few spares just in case. She presses the heavy, foil-wrapped parcels into our hands with a greeting of *Shana Tova*: a good and sweet new year.

Rosh Hashanah is one of the few Jewish holidays I observe, in the loosest possible sense of the word. I am not a member of a synagogue, have never touched a Torah, and know only a few words of Hebrew, committed to memory over more than thirty years. Even so, late September does not feel right unless there is a week where each late afternoon tea break is accompanied by a slice of the sweet, earthy cake, flaked almonds clinging to its sticky top. Its absence would be like Christmas without fishing through a tub of Celebrations for the Maltesers and Galaxys; Easter without mainlining a chocolate egg while still in pyjamas.

For me, honey cake is part of what it means to be Jew-ish. My sister, who undertook a Religious Studies AS Level for the debates, calls us 'Cultural Jews', though the 'us' here refers only to me and her. Our mother is a Scottish shiksa, while my father's Jewishness is not up for debate and most years on Yom Kippur, the holiest day, he fasts to atone for forgetting to replace the Hanukkah candles, his lack of synagogue attendance and consumption of bacon beigels.

A generation later, our family's Scottish-English-Ashkenazi identity is more confused. On filling out a questionnaire, my cursor hovers between the boxes for 'Jewish' and 'no religion'. How do you explain that, despite our godlessness, we have a proclivity to spend holidays in Jewish quarters and at Holocaust memorials; a fondness for *Fiddler on the Roof*, *An American Tail* and even *This is Where I Leave You*? That my knowledge of the Hanukkah story is hazy, but I still look forward to teaching my baby son how to light a menorah, to eating latkes together and spinning the dreidel as the candles melt.

II

The Salt Beef Bar in Temple Fortune serves latkes all year round. Traditionally they are a Hanukkah dish because the grated potato is deep fried in oil, like the oil millenia before it that should only have been enough to keep a lamp burning for one day, yet lasted for eight.

Officially we go to the London takeaway for their eponymous sandwiches, for the soft rye and tender beef and the slick of mustard that is just enough to make you sneeze but not wince. But we can never resist a side of glistening, golden oblongs. They turn the takeaway bag translucent with a grease that slicks our chins and oozes from our foreheads and leaves a sheen on our fingers for the rest of the day, no matter how many times we wash them.

We always eat the sandwiches and the latkes on the parliament-green leather banquette seats in Grandma's kitchen. The takeaway is only acceptable if our visit was very last minute and she hasn't had time to go to Asda. Normally there are three homemade courses, usually preceded by a cup of tea and slice of cake, but not the same cake that you will be served for dessert. If it's a Friday evening, the Shabbat candles flicker softly in the background as we catch up on our news and our friends' news and our latest favourite books and films and television shows.

Yiddish peppers my Grandma's sentences. She says that she cannot speak the language, which her mother brought with her when her family moved from eastern Europe. Once, my husband asked me what a word Grandma had used meant and it caught me off guard; until then I had not thought of the words as another language, for they nestled so comfortably within her English: How are you, *bubbeleh*? Darling, this news, oh, I am *kvelling*.

When she was a preteen, my sister started using Yiddish exclamations: *oy vey* and *oy gevalt* and sometimes just *oy*. But the words were not right in her mouth. She was too conscious of them, like somebody constantly tugging down the hem of a short skirt, and she used them less and less until they faded from her tongue.

III

We congregate as a whole family for Passover and Rosh Hashanah and occasionally as an excuse for a Christmas-cum-Hannukah get-together. On these occasions, when there are too many of us for the kitchen, we migrate to the green-gold dining room where all our graduation and wedding photographs sit proudly on a sideboard. On the speckled wall is a small map of a country Grandma will never go to because it would mean flying and the only time she has flown is when I was eighteen months old and she was allowed to hold me on her knee all the way to Israel.

We arrange ourselves around two tables pushed together, on mismatched seats; losers get the wooden fold-up ones. At Passover, the youngest of the three brothers – the one with the least rusty Hebrew and the synagogue membership – takes his place on the carvery chair at the head of the table, ready to perform the seder. Or at least our truncated, informal version of it.

On this night, the men fish kippahs from the box that surfaces this time each year. They might sport one that is crocheted; one probably meant for a child; one commemorating a bar mitzvah that nobody remembers attending.

On this night, each place is set with the *Haggadah*, the text that gives the order of the service and tells the story of how the Jews escaped slavery in Egypt. There are at least three different translations and so, as we each take it in turns to read a section, much of the evening is spent checking that you are on the right page.

On this night, our arms cross as we pass the oh-so-sweet Manischewitz wine and the foods that we eat to reflect our ancestors' journey. Parsley dipped in saltwater is their tears; sweet apple-walnut charoset on tiny shards of matzah is the clay with which they built the pyramids; bitter raw horseradish is their pain and their suffering and I can only bring myself to nibble at its edges.

On this night, my uncle breaks a piece of matzah in two to transform it into the afikoman, wraps it in cloth. When we were young, Grandpa would hide this in one of three rooms, and after dinner his grandchildren were tasked with seeking it out. The person who found it was rewarded with a bag of kosher sweets. And even though all of us would, in the end, get our own bag, and even though the kosher chocolate was slightly bitter and always left unfinished, the race was always fierce, the winning glorious, the prize from Grandpa treasured.

Nowadays nobody present is young or old enough to take on the challenge. My uncle hides the wrapped matzah beneath a serving plate, because tradition says it is to be saved for dessert. Hours later, I unceremoniously unveil it as we are clearing away the dishes.

The service is just the appetiser, and once we close the *Haggadahs*, dinner begins: four courses served with a side of debates about current affairs and popular culture, with only Brexit off-limits. There is a reassuring familiarity to the meal, to how it is the same every time we gather together. To the slices of Mrs Elswood's pickled cucumbers that my father and his brothers snaffle before we even sit down. To the smooth chopped liver that we spread over soft, sweet challah bread or, at Passover, matzah because at Passover we must only eat unleavened bread. To the crispy, golden fried balls of gefilte fish (mashed carp or hake or haddock or cod) that we cannot help but overeat.

To how one of Grandma's sons will disappear to the kitchen for the Lea & Perrins when the chicken soup is served. To the kneidlach – dumpling-like balls of ground matzah – that float in the hot, slightly yellow liquid, so soft you can slice them open with a spoon.

To how, despite the table getting smaller and quieter over the years, there are always at least three overlapping conversations and conversations within the conversations. To how we have all learnt to participate in at least two of these strands at the same time.

To how the meal finishes with Grandma unveiling a minimum of five desserts, to be shared between, at most, sixteen of us. How among them will be profiteroles that we smother in a thick, warm, dark chocolate sauce and how we will battle over ensuring we have a fair portion of them as fiercely as we did the afikoman decades before. That despite our best efforts, there will be leftovers, and a cake with just one slice taken from it.

On these nights, I wrap myself in my heritage, pull it around me like a heavy blanket on a winter's night. We leave, heading into the dark with our hearts full and bellies straining, carrying Lancashire Farm yoghurt tubs brimming with gefilte fish and chopped liver and cake.

IV

During one of these evenings, in a rare moment away from the dining room, I brushed my hand against one of the mezuzahs that sit quietly in the top corners of Grandma's door frames. I had, I think, just learnt about them in school, that it was customary to do this as you entered a room. But like my sister trying out Yiddish, the gesture felt insincere, as if I was touching something that did not belong to me. I never told anyone that I had tried it.

On the sliding scale of Jewishness, or Jew-ish-ness, when does 'Jewish' become 'no religion'?

Do I lose points for eating hot cross buns at Easter and turkey at Christmas? For listing excuses not to attend a friend's Friday Night Dinner because I worried about feeling out of place, no matter how informal she insisted it would be?

Do I gain them for eating pastrami sandwiches, and rugelach, and bagels and schmear? What does it mean if, when a swastika was scrawled on a bus stop near home, it felt as though someone was squeezing, wringing, my insides; how it made me bow my head and hurry home, where I gasped out tears? Or how about the way I talk with my hands; the multiple occasions on which I have spilt drinks on colleagues and friends during overenthusiastic gesticulations?

'Jewish' or 'no religion'; fraud or betrayal? I press golden crumbs of honey cake into my index finger and lick them off, repeat until my plate is clean. I move my cursor to a box and the question dissolves, moving me on to the next one.

split the bill
the bill

Enough for two

AN APPLE PIE LIFE

TUTKU BARBAROS

Nil always spills her food. Always ends up with it round her mouth, half way down her top, in her teeth. I presume that when she strips, crumbs are always released – set free on the bed – tiny remnants of seeded batch liberated from her baps.

Like a mutiny in a D cup.

She's just out in the garden at the minute. Under a warm south-London sun – you know that sun, yeah?

The sky over south?

South is south, if you know you know.

Always a blue-collar, orange sun glow.

She's picking vine leaves with scissors before tonight's dinner.

The neighbours nip past.

This street is a figurative painting:

you can tell who is from where based on what they're planting.

There's rumour of melons at number 63!

Intrigued neighbours question:

    'Don't you know about how warm it has to be?!'

    'Surely that won't work, surely?!'

While keeping an eye, desperate to see, because if it does work they'll be gagging for a cutting – better still the seeds, please.

Nil is thinking: it's funny that food isn't always something that's made, sometimes it's just something that occurs. That just is. And how much can you apply that rule to other parts of life? Can you apply that to love? No: should you apply that to love?

She's been having a hard time.

She's become over-boiled broccoli.

You know? Something that once had stem and zeal, which survived . . . various (actually!) . . . ordeals now wobbles . . .

                                  . . . is mushy.

She feels as if she's sat in a heavy-bottomed pan surrounded by green. A green which she can't admit is envy. Her outskirts yellowing, as recently she's becoming cowardly.

That's what happens when you've spent time – hours and hours – sat under the fig tree as the CDs which hang from every fucking branch (to ward off every fucking bird) shine shimmery light across the face of you and the love of your life – who . . .

         . . . does not love you back .

                       He does not love you back.

Our houses are packed in close. Our gardens touch. Nil coordinates hanging out her washing with my midday Bloody Mary. Our gardens smell like jasmine, open coals and rolled tobacco. She's got three greenhouses! Three! Which seems strange for someone so young? Gardening always feels like an old person's game, but then again: sustainability, the environment, all of that. And – at the end of the day – I'm the one who has a daily Bloody Mary.

She stretched over one morning. 'I've made about twelve too many, so, do you want some?' Revealing a plate of sesame bread.

'Yeah, that'd be lush – if you're sure, yes.'

I'm guessing that's how she knew Gran. I'm guessing that's how they became friendly.

She never questioned how I came to be here – alone in this big house – less than thirty while she's older and only occupies a ground floor with a garden while working almost constantly.

I presume she knows it all – give or take – anyway – really.

She doesn't need to know that most of my childhood memories involve sitting on curbs beside bookies with my fingers crossed hoping for good news when Daddy comes out.

She doesn't have to know that as all the casinos started to close I was relieved, only to find those bastard adverts transmitted straight to my home.

She mentions Gran a lot and that's nice.

I explain I knew it was the end when I got her one of those massive Christmas bars of chocolate and she immediately misplaced it. You know the ones advertised with that weirdly sexual rabbit?

'How do you misplace half a metre of chocolate?'
        I explained we found it under her pillow.
'Did your nan have chocolate-covered dreams?'
Hopefully.
We both agree she probably did.
And that is kind of lovely.
I didn't know before but: Nil is kind of lovely.

That was how this started really.

Me by myself over here, not completely vulnerable or anything, but always nice to have someone cook for you, innit?

I very rarely ask about him.
Mainly because she tends to volunteer the information herself.
I know she sends photos of what she's cooked with jokes of how she'd be a wonderful wife.
        And he agrees she would
        (and they are both right). But that makes it infinitely worse.

Because then, it's not that he does not love her – but that he will not. And that is something that she thinks she can change. He'd moved in, after all. Had come half the way.

Over time she fills in any gaps I'd clocked. I don't mention his always being in the garden at midnight taking hushed calls, I don't refer to the car that came to stay while she was away. I don't keep quiet for the purpose of secrecy, but because I know she already knows and she deserves some dignity.

*

But I do want to say, I do want to ask:

Imagination mixed with memory turns your heart into an odd brewery. So here's the thing: was it really an apple pie life?

I know there were roast dinners on Sundays.
And yes there were baked cakes.
But surely meals were missed most days?
And yes I always heard the Deliveroo kid slide up on Friday date nights. I heard you both cackle – buoyed by relationship weight – to 'Is there any more room for me in those jeans?'
But there were presumably grabbed lunches? As you separately pursued your dreams?

Sometimes I want to say 'I've got several memories of you pissed, petulant,

way after supper, banging on the door because you forgot your keys'.

But I don't need to go that far in. I can just stick to the bottom line:
Was it really always an apple pie life?

I want to ask that but I don't. It's not my place, really. I just decide to take you as you come.
Nil. As you are.

You ask me what I want, what I fancy, and you always create it. And to start with I lacked imagination, had no ideas, food had always just been food. Sustenance. Affordable. Manageable. It wasn't the sheer fucking essence of life the way it is with you. You're a godsend and a blessing and I really mean it when I suggest you should do this shit for a living. But I do respect that you refuse to because this isn't about earning. This is Saturday afternoons. This is something else. I can never remember what you do anyway, homeopathy? Acupuncture? Masseuse? Something like that. The kind of job that requires you to have dreamcatchers in the window type thing. But I guess, you're doing alright. More alright than me.

A storm destroyed the fence between us, and rather than campaign to the landlord you threw your hands in the air and gave thanks, because now you don't have to traipse up your path then back down mine. You can cut straight to my back door. That was when the eating together started. So now . . . Nil does the dinner and I do the drinks.

Nil didn't eat her feelings – she cooked them instead.
She made a catharsis out of chopped courgettes.
    re-built a home out of half-risen bread.
        love songs out of mind, recipes instead.
I'm not sure when but at some point superstition also stirred into the mix?
        She would be disturbed by egg shells crashing on the floor
Apparently that brings terrible luck (according to some folklore?)
            Committed to salt flying over her left shoulder
                Straight in the eye of the devil she fears
behind her
            Seven stirs of water to half a spoon of sugar.
Now we read our coffee cup fortunes, for more than just the culture
And this time we spend feels more and more . . .

                            together.

        I bullshit you, you bullshit me, but sometimes just some-
times in the well of that spilt coffee we share our deepest dreams and

whether or not we are making it up or totally gifted feels irrelevant because spirits are always lifted.

We sit we talk we chat. She brings fresh mint that she smashes into the side of the glass to get all the flavour out. We joke that ginger looks like aliens. That the artichokes she's growing do too – and sometimes at night the wind blows them side to side in a way I find quite alarming. She tells me not to be silly and carries on reciting articles about urban farming. We joke she should get a chicken, selfishly I put her off the idea – she alone makes enough bloody noise.

She shows me new kitchen gadgets the way a kid would show me toys. Garlic crushers are a waste of time, she tells me. But this new onion chopper thing is a game changer. It's got to the point that I can barely believe Nil was ever stranger. We talk about sexual harassment over thick-cut fries. When we've eaten too much we compare the shape of our thighs. I ask her things over avocados and sometimes she makes things just for aesthetic purposes: a salad of red cabbage – which should be called purple cabbage – and radishes – which would be called pink turnips – and carrots which . . . obviously . . . can't be called oranges. All of it, all colourful.

She makes hummus from scratch. And she never buys guac.

She makes things the way her mum has taught her, and I wonder if even though our age gap is less than ten years she sees me as a kind of daughter.

Right now she stands leaves in hand.

About to go from tree to sink.

Before placing the mixture in the middle

Folding each side then roll, roll, roll,
Not too leafy
not leafless either
cook it under pressure
and bash it on a plate.

I love her, I love her how pomegranate seeds love their shell.

She tells me tonight she spent some time in hospital once. They fed her warm Weetabix, two slices of white bread and a little packet of jam. Ever since, she's believed that's the breakfast of a healing hand.

I ask if she has it every day.

No why would I?

And I believe her.

She's grown glorious in her heart-break and by proxy so have I.

We were two different shades of grief, separated by a fence, and now that fence has a serving hatch. A gap we sit between. A gap we fill with clattering forks.

Nan knew her mum, used to mention her a lot actually
And from what I gather they're quite similar. Naturally.
Parallel relationships I guess?
Always two sides of a fence.

Biting into 63's melons, which worked out alright – not perfect but alright – good with halloumi (but then again, what isn't?). Sipping tart citric bubbly homemade lemonade – my forte – her door knocks, we look over and see. It's him.

She jumps up, I motion at her to wipe that foody mouth.

Thankful for the heads up, she does.

She tells me to stay where I am as she goes to the door. I feel nervous.

I hear him explain that he's realised what he did was wrong. It's the verbal equivalent of a Twitter apology from a well-known but not super famous comedian – you know, puts the blame on her a bit? While somehow still marketing himself? Saying that he'll learn from it? With no clear indication of how?

And though I know she's come a long way, I notice she never sits under the fig tree anymore and, given how good the tanning potential is, I presume that's because she maybe misses him just too much to sit there in that spot?

When she closes the door for a second, and re-opens it to reveal a box

I feel a relief I can't explain.

Point taken, he grabs it and starts to walk away, not before stopping to make one last attempt: I can come and fix your fence?

'The fence is great as it is,' she says, waving him away.

He steps closer and sees me now.

Says hi and asks about my nan. As I answer, the door clacks shut and Nil makes her way back to me. It dawns on him that this is our table and our spread.

His eyebrows raise.

'Oh right, I never really knew you two were friends?'

He looks at me suspicious, knowing I know all his indiscretions.

It almost makes me laugh that he still doesnt realise that all of us – Nil included – from 1 to 105 do. Especially the ones at number 42.

Nil doesn't look up, instead she diligently slices fruit and arranges it on a plate. Loquats (or 'New Worlds' as they're known in Turkish), grapes and segments of orange.

'Glad to see you're still getting your vitamin C,' he says.

She nods and looks up at him as if to ask 'what did you expect?'

He sighs, and walks away from a life that could have been his and is now somehow mine.

An apple pie life.

FEAST
OR FOE

ETTIE BAILEY-KING

'Maeve. This one's for you,' Duncan barked. She'd been about to say '*But I'm almost entirely vegetarian*' when he said, 'I can't waste any of my better writers on this one,' and moved on. She swayed slightly, like when a freight train slams past you on a station platform. He was gone before she could compose a sentence that felt polite but firm, reminding him that vegetarianism is '*an environmental necessity right now, not just an ethical one.*' It was too late.

She got to the restaurant at one minute to six, and winced through all of the tasting menu's seven courses. Maeve never gets a plus one when she's reviewing on the magazine's money. Everybody else does. Her expense limit is the lowest at the paper, so she can't just swipe their credit card. She has to pay out of her own pocket, and wait the four to six humiliating weeks to be reimbursed. Other writers have company cards with generous expense limits. Maeve overheard Sarah in accounts telling someone that Holly Gore has no expense limit at all.

The third course in the tasting menu is liver with tart green apple. The acid brightness of the apple lights up the dark depth of liver. Yin and yang. Like me and Holly, she thinks. Holly is pale, lean, long, so clumsy it's graceful. Maeve is soft, dark, brown, short. And she's deliberate: slow, heavy molasses to Holly's ditzy icing sugar.

Holly Gore: golden girl. A curtain of swishing hair the colour of rust. A dusting of freckles on her perfectly crooked nose. Teeth bright white and perfectly straight. Her voice is hoarse and sensual, her limbs so slim you could snap them.

She Instagrams sourdough bloomers and glossy challah like they're accidents: *I made crumpets wtf*. She tears her herbs because *she doesn't even own kitchen scissors, I know, I know*. Maeve has read in countless cookbooks that tearing herbs is the best way to avoid bruising their delicate leaves and so tears her herbs like a soldier following orders. But Holly tears them with abandon. *Just all the shit I had in my vegetable crisper* she captions another 'gram of ruby beets, arugula, dill, artisanal feta and cubes of homemade sourdough.

Maeve has been watching Holly's sourdough. It is suspiciously accomplished. She wants to ask what level of hydration Holly is following, and when does she add the salt to the autolyse? Maeve wants to ask her what temperature her kitchen tends to be (her artsy, *tiny, like I can't even lift my arms, there's only room for making margaritas* kitchen). Maeve knows every angle of the kitchen, because it's where Holly and her friends (beautiful; asymmetric haircuts) sometimes Instagram their 4 a.m. karaoke sessions. But she can't see what temperature it is, not from Instagram.

Maeve creates a new email address to set up her Twitter and Instagram profiles. They all belong to a thirty-two-year-old called

Brandon, with a good-looking, but not too good-looking, photo she found on Reddit. It's important nobody sees her lurking. To the outside observer, studying someone else's life like this just means you're sore about your own. But that's not it, not at all.

The next course is a Bolognese made with chicken liver. She rolls her spoon across the surface to pick up pools of golden fat.

What's the algorithm for Holly Gore? What makes it all work? The dusting of freckles, the angular charm of her limbs? Maeve pulls out her phone and googles 'cost of getting freckles tattooed on face'. It's a lot. *Whatever.*

By the time the last course rolls round, Maeve's stomach is churning. She shuffles to the disabled restroom and coils up in pain. A gurgle, then a sudden lurch. She's in there a long time. They're shutting up the restaurant. A kind waitress explains for the third time that Maeve will need to leave, and Maeve croaks that she understands, she'll be right out. She's finished every roll of toilet paper in the stall, so there's nothing to mop her streaked mascara with. Maeve wets her fingers and swipes underneath each eye, only smearing her makeup more.

She has to split the bill across three credit cards. Maeve tries to smile winningly at the server. The server's eyes linger on her face, taking in the streaming wet eyes and flushed cheeks.

Outside into the roaring cold of New York. A blast of wind rips through her cheap coat and stops her in the doorway. As she hovers there, a group of women crash into her. They're wearing cropped wide-legged pants and ankle boots, light coats on this icy black night. One of them has a curtain of russet hair that shines under the violent light of the streetlamp.

'Maeve? Maeve!' Holly screams. Her friends are singing, gurgling, giggling. Two of them have broken away to dance in the street, while a third one records it on her phone.

'Oh hey, Holly.' Maeve feels a sickening lurch, as though she's missed a step while going downstairs.

'You okay?' Holly eyes Maeve's smudged makeup, the sheen of sweat on her forehead. She takes in the rumpled air of excess.

Think fast.

'Sure, sure. I just went for drinks with my friend and – woah, where'd he go?' Maeve wheels around in mock confusion.

'Man down? Now that's a big night.' Holly's face crumples into a grin. 'Come with us.'

She's in an Uber. One of the girls has her handbag in Maeve's face. Another bleats at the driver until he plays Peggy Goo. They arrive in Williamsburg, at a space that Maeve can't place. Is it someone's home, a gallery, a shop? It's vast. Exposed brick walls stretch far above Maeve's head. So do the guests. Everybody here is tall, so tall and so well dressed.

'This is Maeve,' Holly says, to everyone that comes over to say hi. They're talking to her. They eye her with a look that Maeve doesn't recognise. She sees herself through their eyes – *a friend of Holly's.*

Someone brings her an espresso martini, someone takes her jacket for her. There's a DJ, a kind of abstract music she hasn't heard before. Howls of laughter erupt all around. Her stomach groans, but she keeps on drinking. She stretches her mouth into a smile. And now it's three, now it's four a.m. and they're piling into another Uber.

Sirens howling. Fist fight. Wet cobbles. Trash steaming on a street corner. Headlamps in the rain. Pearls of light.

Holly opens the front door. Maeve knows her way. She knows how the front door opens right on to Holly's bed, at the centre of the little studio. She knows how *monstera* and *zamioculcas* flow around the windows and walls, and trailing ivy drifts from a rattan pot. She's seen the faded pink sofa a hundred times, Holly's drunk friends and famous restaurant critics and good-looking, dishevelled men propped up on it swigging negronis as the early morning light filters through the floor-to-ceiling windows. Maeve doesn't know anyone else in their twenties who lives alone in the city.

As the other guests pile on to the velvet sofa or into the tiny kitchen and start glugging wine into tumblers and mugs, Maeve marches to the bathroom. Her cramps are savage. She finds pain-killers in the cupboard and swallows two, then practices looking relaxed in the mirror.

She inspects the room. There's a postcard from Chez Panisse Blu-Tacked on to the wall, some over-exposed polaroids of meals: tiny bowls of paella and *jamon*, a granita, a pile of pistachios taller than Maeve. Books pour off the shelves, pooling around the foot of the bed. Alice Waters, Julia Child, Nigel Slater. And unlike Maeve's books, there is no forest of Post-its fanning out, just the bruise of thumbprints on page corners, the occasional slop of blood-red tomato slashed across a page.

There's a gallery wall, with some prints Maeve can't place, and a big pennant with a skull-and-crossbones. There are framed photos, too. Sun-drenched summer photos, the boardwalk in her Maine hometown, a basket of apples. And a shot of a big white house, a brace of good-looking girls and boys baring expensive orthodontic smiles. Three golden, happy dogs out front. *White people always know whether it's a golden retriever or a Labrador*, she thinks. She makes a note on her phone to google it later.

She recognises the house. She's seen it in Holly's #throwback posts. Photos of skinny girls in shorts and swimsuits laughing out front, playing with those dumb dogs. There's a distinctive shape to the lake opposite Holly's house. It made it easy to find on Google Earth.

On the kitchen countertop, Holly's sourdough starter is bubbling away. The girls from earlier tumble into the bedroom and start slicing up lines on the desk. Maeve hears a chorus of snorts as they each hoover up a wedge of white, then the babble resumes at twice the speed.

Maeve opens the cupboard doors. She finds a bottle of 150-year-aged balsamic vinegar, pops the cork and lets the rich, dark aroma flood her nostrils. She pours it into Holly's sourdough starter, and smiles as it starts to hiss and fizz.

Monday morning. Maeve styles her hair and follows every step of a YouTube tutorial called 'get that no-make-up glow'. It involves a lot of make-up. Choosing her clothes is harder. How drab her black shirts and trousers look. Eventually she settles for a calf-length, tight-fitting grey dress. It looks a little like a dead sealskin, but it passes for stylish. She's so sweaty from the subway she dips into the bathroom in the lobby to refresh her makeup, comb her hair.

'Morning!' Holly dives into the elevator after her. Cheeks flushed from her cycle ride, a Yale scarf dangling dangerously down to her knees, waist so narrow Maeve imagines cracking it like a wishbone.

Maeve is ready. She prepared some casual remarks – they reek of spontaneity. It took her all weekend to prepare, but it was worth the hours spent speaking to her bathroom cabinet to hear herself now, bouncing banter back and forth like she's always been this chill. Holly laughs, throwing back her slender face. The slight bulge of her larynx throbs at her thin white neck.

Later that day, and after two years of working together at the same magazine, Holly follows Maeve on Twitter. Her real account, not Brandon the cyber-lurker.

In Monday's editorial meeting, it's the regular rabid bullfight to pitch stories. Mac yells about new food trends and Duncan asks why nobody on his staff can write for shit. Almost nobody, he says, with a nod to Holly.

The meeting runs over. The busier writers start to filter out as the clock creaks past nine. Holly slips away, Duncan says nothing. Maeve tries to follow in her slipstream.

'Hold it! Does it look like this meeting's over? I'm still talking.'

Maeve withers back into her seat.

'One more thing. We can't run that feature with Marco Biber. Sex scandal or something. So I need a piece that can go, right now. Who's sitting on something?'

A few interns pipe up with suggestions. Duncan ignores them. Maeve, imagining herself coated with a fine dusting of gold that has rubbed off from Holly, clears her throat.

'I've got one. The greatest food scenes of all time, from literature. Not the obvious ones, no dull re-hashings of Proust's madeleine. It's kinda quirky. There's Madame Bovary, but also a murder mystery where the weapon's a frozen leg of lamb.'

She has been practising all weekend, so she knows what it feels like to telegraph utter, disinterested confidence. Take it or leave it. The hint of a smile plays over the corners of her lips.

'Send it over,' says Duncan. And then there's a screeching of chairs being pushed back, and a flurry of feet out the door.

*

Maeve's piece is a hit. Light, breezy, effortless. No one needs to know it took almost three years to write. Masterpieces take time, Maeve says to herself in the mirror. They need to ferment.

For her next article, she asks the entire magazine staff for an unforgettable food memory. There are sun-drenched stories of Greek taverna, grilled pineapple on Thai beaches and lobsters dripping butter in New England. There's a perfect pluot – *that's a cross between a plum and an apricot, if you didn't know.* There's burnt butter and brown butter, fennel dust and gulls' eggs with celery salt. There are words that Maeve can't even begin to spell. She records them all as a voice note, then uses voice assistant to google them. Masterpieces take time.

Maeve sees Holly on her way to the restroom and jumps up. They bump into each other at the door.

'Oh my gosh, great question.' Holly chews her lip. 'So I think it would be the first time I went to Europe, to stay with this girl I knew from my high school – oh, it was a boarding school,' she adds helpfully.

Maeve nods, like someone who hasn't looked up all of Holly's photos from when she was captain of the field hockey team.

'So I fly to Nice to stay with Manon, and like the small-town kid I am, all I've packed is shorts and sweatshirts from the Gap! Can you imagine? Ugh. All her French friends were so chic. I was a total fish out of water.

'I guess my foodie awakening was when I came down to breakfast to these piles of pastries, and I go to pick up a croissant. It falls apart, it splinters into tiny shards, and I realise that this is the first real croissant I've ever tried, you know? Like, what I was eating back in Maine wasn't even a croissant.'

Holly pronounces croissant *kwa-sohhh.*

Maeve's food memories are different. They sweat with the fog of her childhood home, a tiny apartment over a dry cleaners. She remembers slicing up tripe for *xiaolongbao* with her *nai nai*, steaming up every window when she made carp soup, taking rice and vegetables down to her mom as she worked another night shift. But she's interviewed enough of the other writers at the magazine to know that your life-changing food moment should involve pastry, or Europe. So she invents a trip to summer camp – an obscure one, somewhere in New England, she's careful never to say what years she went there – and a Portugese pastry chef whose *pastéis de nata were just sublime.*

In the office, the women are talking about their worst dates. Sarah tells everyone about a date with an awkward, nerdy guy who took her to a murder-mystery play.

'It was totally kitsch. The detective literally jumped out on the murderer and caught him in the act. I thought he was gonna take me to *Hamilton*, and *that's* what I got.' The others howl with laughter.

Maeve drifts past the group on her way to the coffee machine. She pantomimes a conspiratorial laugh, as if to say *how camp, how ridiculous.* But Maeve has always loved murder mysteries. The neatness, the promise of explanation. The perfect order of a universe in which every crime – however mysterious or incomprehensible – is neatly laid to rest by the end.

She likes the known hierarchies. Aristocratic murderers are at the top, but even the working-class detective can fell them. Everything comes to order, the good and bad are found out. No more the confusing hierarchies of daily life, where the quality of your sour-dough or the shininess of your hair predict whether people like you.

She loves their precision. The frozen leg of lamb, the perfect murder weapon.

It's a baking hot day and her roommates are out sunbathing. She spreads her research materials across the living room floor.

'In a village called Pont-Saint-Esprit in 1951, the villagers started to go insane. Not gently, but with howling and fits. They suffered convulsions, hallucinations, boils . . . the most medieval of afflictions. Some threw themselves out of windows to escape their visions, and others just died. Nobody could explain it. But now, we may know why. Who's heard of ergotism?' A pause. 'It's a blight caused by slightly damp grain. Their grain stores weren't watertight.'

In junior year, Maeve's history professor had gone on a strange tangent. Maeve took reams of notes that day, trying to get every single detail down. After class she ran back to her room, mumbled hi to her roommate, and settled down to study.

The idea of ergotism settled into Maeve like rot. It bubbled and festered inside. It would come to her when she was cooking, or writing, or when she was having sex, mind drifting back to those rotting bins of grain, the mystery nobody could solve.

And it comes back to her again, now, as she sucks the end of a biro at her tiny desk.

Feast or foe: the curious history of culinary murder.

Maeve doesn't mention this to anyone. She sticks with dumb, effervescent pieces: cocktails from classic books, tequila ten ways, what your favourite bar snack says about you. She carves out an unthreatening space in the magazine – *just a bit of fun.*

She closes her laptop and starts to write in her notebook. But then she frowns, opens her laptop up and googles 'does cooking destroy ergot'. Damn. It does. Sourdough won't work. *Wouldn't* work. It's all just research.

What about Roald Dahl's *Lamb to the Slaughter*? Oh, yes. Loving wife Mary Moloney waits for her policeman husband to come home. When he announces he's leaving her, she swings a frozen leg of lamb at his head and knocks him down dead. She cooks up the leg of lamb and serves it to the colleagues that come to investigate his murder. 'The murder weapon [is] probably right under our noses,' they say as they chew up the lamb. And then there's the icicle that kills the murderer in *The Lovely Bones*. Like a jagged bolt of lightning out of the sky, it rains down vengeance.

A perfect murder weapon melts away. Or it slow-roasts until tender, falling off the bone, rich with anchovy paste and served with sweet green petits pois.

Yes, that would be perfect.

The office is quiet on a Friday. It's early, earlier than their contracted finish time, when Holly texts Maeve: *I'm finished already, you good to leave in five?*

Maeve has never left early before.

Sure, let me just grab my stuff.

Her bag is packed. She has everything she needs. Maeve sets a timer for four minutes, then stands up. 'I'm ready!'

LOVE IS...
L'AMORE É...

LUCY PORTER

1

...the 'plink' of the doorbell. Every day, you climb the shallow, stone steps from your apartment to ours, to ask if we need any dinner that evening. Standing at the edge of our home, your voice is low and gentle. Your eyes hide behind your glasses and you look away, as if you were shy of M – your son, my partner. He answers (*si grazie*) and you sink into a pensive quiet, still standing there in the doorway but your mind already sorting through the cupboards downstairs – what will you cook for dinner tonight?

2

...laughter on a sultry evening. It flows from the other side of the *villa*, far away but close in my ear, like music heard underwater. We have journeyed south to Salento for a week, the very tip of the heel to the mainland's boot. It is our first holiday together. You are in the kitschiest of kitchens, rinsing the feathery, aromatic clumps of *finocchietto selvatico* that your best friend has brought up from Sicily. His voice trumpets through the bare white rooms as the two of you make art of the vegetables picked up at the market and the fish bought straight off the boat. M and I drag the plastic table onto the veranda and dress it with an old tablecloth found deep in a stiff drawer. The day's heat idles in the stone beneath our toes. I bring a floor lamp outside, set it aglow at the head of the table, and our stage has been set. We stay outside long after the mosquitos come.

3

...an open front door. Every day, we descend to your apartment and let ourselves in without knocking. Sunlight pools on the stairs outside your door. It is always summer here. M calls you by your nickname as we enter to the familiar music of the floorboards. The kitchen windows have been thrown open, and outside the sun drops like a heavy peach into the Milanese rooftops. You tend to the cluster of pots simmering over the flames. We pull the chairs scraping across the tiles, set the beaded placemats on the table with a *clack*, fill the carafe with water from the tap. You take a bottle of wine from the fridge and pour an inch into each of our tumblers, condensation frosting the glass.

4

...a table wobbling on uneven paving stones. You and I are out for dinner at the restaurant we take all our British visitors to, with its red-and-white checked table cloths and the candles that drip cathedrals of wax down the necks of old wine bottles. The food is cheap but good, and it could almost be the real deal if it weren't for the fact that this bistro is called Carlsberg and you can dine on asparagus at any time of year here. M is not with us tonight – instead, my mother takes his place at the table. The time has finally come for our families to meet, and she is staying with us for a week. You and I have decided to take her out for dinner this evening, in a good-humoured attempt to teach M a lesson for abandoning his guests in favour of his regular board game night. The joke is on me though – my mother doesn't speak a word of Italian beyond the obligatory *gelato* and *vino*, and you do not speak English. We sit in the blue blush of dusk, the city heat still prickling my skin and the mosquitoes close about our ears. Alpine swifts wheel above the remains of the old canals, their high-pitched screeches circling through the air. I hardly notice a thing as I desperately scrabble to translate our conversation into both languages. When the food arrives, I hardly get a moment to chew, scarfing my pasta down whole. When the bottles of wine we've been sipping force me to head to the bathroom, I apologise profusely and dash off as quickly as I can, desperate to relieve you both of an awkward discussion made up only of gestures and smiles. But when I come back I can barely believe my ears. You, having never spoken a word to me that wasn't Italian, are chatting to my mum in perfect English.

5

...the hiss of the fire beneath the grate. Every day, we watch you as you prepare our meal. You waltz around the kitchen, moving to the rhythm of your own somnambulant melody. I look over your shoulder at the pans, at the quick slip of the knife against onions, tomatoes, garlic. There's barely a finger on your hands that doesn't speak of some kitchen mishap or other, trips to A & E recalled in a misshapen thumb, or a fingernail that never quite grew back. Seeing you now, I can't imagine you making a mistake. Sometimes you try to teach me on those days when I am studying at home. We stand side by side at the wooden counter, and I watch in horror as you scrub the innards from a small, silvery sardine with your thumb, and dump them in the sink. I manage two before I slink back to my studies. But I return the favour by cooking for you occasionally. I am so proud of my three-course meal, which you and M polish from your plates. Years later I cringe at the memory, at the fact that I added pomegranate and feta to your traditional fennel-and-orange salad recipe. But you never said a word.

6

...a quiet side road in a tourist town. M and I follow you, a figure engulfed in your heavy winter coat. You take us into a nondescript bakery, all strip lighting and Perspex cases, and we peer at the fat balls coated in tangerine breadcrumbs behind the plastic. I leave with two of them nestled in my palms, their warmth soaking into my hands through the flimsy paper napkins. We find a bench and get to work. Crisp breadcrumbs give way to the satisfying stodge of yesterday's risotto. They break apart lazily in our hands as we eat, unearthing a molten core like that of this volcanic island. *Arancini* – literally, little oranges. But nothing like the flavourless staple of the British pub's vegetarian menu – these are stuffed with Sicily. One *alla Norma*, that heady concoction of fried aubergine, tomatoes and *ricotta salata* cheese, and one threaded with *finochietto selvatico* and sardines. *'Queste sono gli arancini piu buoni della mia vita!'* – these are the best arancini of my life – I say in my broken Italian, and the two of you laugh because I have been saying this about everything I have eaten since we arrived on this island, your childhood home. These trips around Italy are becoming part of our yearly rhythms, as dependable as the heartbeat of the tides. I thought we had so many more of them left.

7

...a plateful of pasta after a long day. Every day, a steaming pan is brought to the table, and the day's worries dissipate with the vapour. Tonight you have made *calamarata*, a favourite of yours. The giant halos of pasta are almost indistinguishable in size and shape from the soft white *calamari* they are tumbled together with – sometimes it's not until you pop a tomato-splattered forkful into your mouth that you find out which it is. Or it could be that *spaghetti alle vongole* is on the menu, long strands of pasta licked by the sea with those tiny little morsels to be teased from shells the size of mermaids' fingernails. Or it might be large tubes of *rigatoni* lost in a tomato sauce that has been stewing all afternoon, gilded with oily slithers of aubergine and delicate curls of *ricotta salata*. You have spent so much time putting this together for us. I wonder what you eat on the nights you dine alone. You fill our plates, once, twice. *Finiamolo* – let's finish it – you say.

8

...a polystyrene carton of *gelato*. M and I stand at the counter, choosing the flavours we think you'd like best. Sharp raspberry *sorbetto*, creamy *fior di latte*, an almost floral *pistacchio*. I add a bag of buttery, lemony *lingue di gatto* biscuits which we can use to spoon the thick, cold cream out and onto our tongues. Then we stroll home again, through the Milanese springtime that sweeps in golden light through the old avenues. The trams play their mournful song as they scrape along the rails towards the pink wedding cake of the Duomo. We bring you a bowl to your armchair, the tyranny of good habits abandoned by now. You're allowed anything you like when you're sick, and every time we leave the apartment, we return with some delight or other, like today's ice cream or a paper bag patterned with oily fingerprints and stuffed full of fresh, salty *focaccia*. We are still happy.

9

...an ordinary feast. Every day, we dine as though it were our last chance. We chase the pasta with a gratin built of delicate slips of potato, silvery fresh sardines and slabs of tomato. Or the simple delight of a boiled egg, a few legs of asparagus, and a drizzle of the olive oil brought up from Calabria by a friend. Or the gravadlax that has lain encased beneath salt and sugar for days, bejewelled like a king in its juniper berries. Once a platter of oysters, which you split apart like a stonecutter unearthing hidden gems. Leftovers are rare. It is often at this point in the meal that you surprise us with your latest plans – '*ragazzi*, I'm going to China for a month. Next week.' – or some other last-minute, far-flung plans that will take you off and away on another adventure for a while.

10

...one less plate at the table. Week by week, the journey from your armchair to the kitchen table grows more strenuous. Ordinary things become gradually impossible. One day you pick up a mussel and bite straight into its night-sky shell. Then you stop leaving your bed at all. M convinces one of your favourite restaurants to sell their first ever takeaway. From your bedroom, you have your last ever four-course meal, your last ever taste of dishes like *cacio e pepe*, Romanesco cauliflower with candied lemon peel. Then the pasta stops, the *secondi* are finished, and it is meal after meal of soft, mushy soups, tipped carefully into your mouth until one day the palliative care nurse tells us quietly to stop. For days now you have barely woken. Feeding you has meant watching every tiny mouthful and gently calling your name to make sure that you don't drift off before swallowing. Now they tell us not to bring you food anymore – the risk of choking, your clearly stated wish for withdrawal of treatment... You have always fed us and put such delicious love on our plates, and we must repay this with an absence.

And then you are only at our table in memory.

II

...that moment of silence when the last words fall. Every day, the words slowly stop, and the three of us sit wrapped in the quiet, listening to the gentle whirring of the fridge as we finish our wine. Then the plates are rinsed and stacked in the dishwasher, and a damp cloth is passed over the table top. We slide the table back against the wall and push the chairs in underneath. Once everything is back in its place, we pause in the doorway to say goodnight to you. The sound of your voice is soft in the evening air. And then we climb back up the stairs, knowing we will dine together again tomorrow.

taste buds

Discovering new flavours

OF BLOOD AND BLOOMING FLOWERS

ALICE SLATER

It started with mince. Spongy and pink, marbled with fat, prim in a plastic tray. It was a bright Sunday morning, and I was frying a soffritto of diced onions, carrots and celery for a bolognese. I always cleaned the kitchen, then cooked on a Sunday morning. Soups, stews, pasta sauces. Stuff we could freeze in batches and microwave during the week.

The meat was on the counter next to tins of chopped tomatoes and an apothecary of dried herbs: oregano, thyme, bay. I liked to set everything out before I began, and I cleaned up as I went, so I could really focus on the hypnotic power of chopping, stirring, simmering.

Sophie staggered into the kitchen, bent double like a figure from a Wilfred Owen poem, arms wrapped around her lower belly.

'Are you finally coming on?' I said, stirring the vegetables in their fragrant slick of oil.

She flipped on the kettle and leaned against the counter. 'I swear to god, Brenna, I'm going to die.'

'Ah, the miracle of mother nature at work.'

'You're not funny.'

Sophie was beautiful, but she only felt beautiful after a few laborious hours in front of the mirror. In that moment, she looked drained as she fingered an angry-looking spot on her chin, but she always seemed a bit peaky without her makeup.

'Are you in or out tonight? I don't mind, but I want to know how much of this I should freeze,' I said.

'Save me some,' she said. 'I'm seeing Daniel, but I don't know.'

She'd been seeing-but-I-don't-knowing Daniel for several months. Each week she floated the idea of breaking things off, and each week she came home hungry and cosmically fucked instead. He was a vegan and they only ever seemed to eat cold falafel straight from the packet, day-old hummus with stale pita bread, lentil curries that had been left to boil on the hob for hours while he talked about big pharma and chemtrails and all the ways in which we let the government control us – with birth control, with social media, with reality TV, all while chain-smoking roll-up cigarettes that stained his teeth and fingers yellow.

'He'll never fall out of love with you if you keep sleeping with him,' I said.

The kettle clicked. She poured boiling water into a peach-coloured mug and added a teabag. 'He's not in love with me,' she said, absentmindedly poking a finger into the slab of mince, up to the first knuckle. I gave her hand a little slap with my wooden spoon.

'He hardly knows me,' she said. 'He does most of the talking. That's what I like about him. I can just kind of drift. He doesn't expect anything from me.'

'He's in love with how you make him feel,' I said.

Daniel was a philosophy student. He had serious, beautiful eyes, a Kabbalah bracelet and strong opinions on how to take care of himself and the planet. He said goodbye with a respectful bow, eyes closed, hand pressed to his heart, regardless of who he was speaking to. Drunk and feeling particularly ungenerous, Sophie once admitted – to my delighted howls – that before he became vegan, he used to wash his hair once a week with a raw egg, beaten into a foam with a fork.

'He's in love with how I make his dick feel,' she shrugged. Then she placed a lump of raw mince the size of a marble into her mouth.

'Sophie! Did you just eat that?'

Her eyes bulged, and she spat it into her hand, a little tooth-marked ball of bubble-gum-pink meat. 'I honestly don't know why I just did that,' she said, flinging it into the sink and taking a draught of hot tea to rinse her mouth. 'I honestly don't know why.'

The following day, we went to see our friend Maggie's play in the basement of a bar in Islington. We sat in the dark with pints of Guinness ('I need the fucking iron,' Sophie said), and our drinks gradually grew warm and flat as we sipped politely and tried not to fidget. It was a gender-swapped *Dracula*, and Maggie played the Countess; bright fake blood like strawberry syrup down her chin, sliding between her breasts, coating her plastic fangs. It was embarrassing but we loved her enough to stay for the second half.

'I'm ravenous,' Sophie said afterwards, in the bar. Maggie, pale skin stained red, was drinking prosecco with her director-boyfriend, surrounded by a bunch of her theatre friends. They were the kind of people who liked to do sing-alongs to showtunes, even when sober. They were not our people.

'Can we eat?'

'They have a pizza oven here,' I said. 'D'you want to share a pepperoni or something?'

'No, I need *real* meat,' she replied, knocking back the dregs of her pint and giving Maggie a thumbs-up across the room. Maggie gave us a dramatic wave and pantomimed a flurry of kisses, just as some bore started to bang out a few bars on the piano and the crowd around her cheered.

'Just in the nick of time,' I said, holding the door open for Sophie.

'Those freaks have been eyeing up that piano all night. It was only a matter of time.'

The high street was clotted with smokers standing outside the bars in clumps. We weaved between them, arm in arm.

'I finally came on,' she said to me, pushing open the door of Pam's, an American-style diner with bright haemoglobin-red leather seats.

'Can we not talk about that right this second?' I said.

'Alright,' she said. 'Calm down.'

We took a booth and ordered cheeseburgers and garlic fries, onion rings, Cokes.

'Oh – can I get my burger extra rare please?' Sophie said, folding her menu and handing it to our server.

'Sure thing – and for you, hon?' The waitress was dumpy in a cute way, and she spoke with an American lilt, like she'd been in London for a while but still thought of stars and stripes when she thought of home. She had a little silver heart pendant around her throat.

'Well-done,' I said. 'Like, *really* well-done. Thanks so much.'

'You should get it medium, at least,' Sophie said, taking a paper straw from a glass on the table in anticipation of her drink. 'It tastes better when it's not overcooked.'

'I don't like the blood,' I said. 'And the way rare meat is kind of lukewarm. It makes me feel sick.'

'Daniel wants me to go vegetarian,' she said. 'I said maybe, but to be honest I don't think I could go without meat.'

'You don't even like him that much! Why would you think about changing your diet for him?'

'I don't know,' she said as our server delivered our cokes, large sundae glasses spitting silver bubbles. 'It wouldn't be *for* him. Like coming off the pill wasn't *for* him. It would be for the planet, for my health. I don't know. Not right now though. Part of the reason I went on the pill in the first place was cos of my anaemia. My period was so heavy, I kept fainting.'

'I think you should probably just enjoy your burger then,' I said. She looked pale, the colour of cottage cheese, even though she was fully made up. Her eyes were smudged with a mixture of kohl and the bruised bags of a bad night's sleep. 'Does your doctor know you've come off the pill?'

'I'll make an appointment,' she said absently, stirring her Coke, chin in hand.

'That kind of worries me, Soph. I don't really understand why you stopped taking it.'

'I was just sick of it, that's all. All the chemicals and stuff. I don't know. Chill out.'

Our food arrived in red plastic baskets lined with greaseproof paper printed with the name of the restaurant. When Sophie lifted her burger, watery pink blood puddled in the paper folds, dappled with spots of oil. It soaked into her fries, bled into the bun, softened the batter of her onion rings. She didn't seem to mind, but the sight of all that red turned my stomach.

*

Sophie was a messy flatmate. Overworked by med school and out most nights, she left a wake of crumpled tissues around the flat, a scattering of magazines on the carpet by the sofa, plastic takeaway containers gummed with sweet and sour sauce by the kitchen sink. The kitchen table was invisible under an ever-shifting tundra of textbooks, handbag detritus, crumbed plates, glasses and mugs, makeup, unopened post, tangled headphones, empty wine bottles, soiled face wipes and notebooks tightly packed with her neat bubble-writing that wasn't in keeping with her otherwise chaotic presence.

After lectures, while Sophie was smoking salvia at Daniel's or working late in the library, I stacked magazines and collected plates, sorted the mail, wiped surfaces, hoovered up crumbs, hair and fingernail clippings. Tidying up after Sophie never bothered me, and I was used to her overly present presence, even in her absence.

But the smell, the smell that lingered in the bathroom, was new.

There was a permanent tang of metal in the air, even when I emptied the overflowing bin and bleached the toilet bowl and left the bathroom window cracked open all day. I wondered if it was some form of unconscious internalised misogyny making me hallucinate the smell of blood, perhaps because we were talking about menstruation so much, and Sophie liked to keep me updated on the heft of her flow. I bought an expensive geranium reed diffuser and placed it on the cistern with a rose-scented candle and a can of air freshener called 'Spring Day', but it just made the bathroom smell sickly, of blood and blooming flowers.

Sophie was sitting on the living room floor in jogging bottoms and an old Metallica T-shirt, a hot water bottle cradled in her lap like a kitten. She was watching an old horror film on the television. Something with howling werewolves, a full moon and a strangely snazzy soundtrack.

'Daniel broke up with me,' she said in a voice thick with mucus. 'I've been bleeding for ten days, and now he's broken up with me.'

'You don't even like him that much,' I said, leaning against the door jamb. 'And honestly, I think you need to go to your doctor.'

'Some sympathy would be nice,' she sulked.

'I'm sorry – but you know I never liked him. And you know I think you should have gone to your doctor ages ago.'

On-screen, a sweat-speckled man screamed. His skin split down the seam of his spine to reveal a thick pelt. 'I always thought if I broke things off, it would break his heart. But he just sent a text and that's that. Said he needed to focus on *other things*. What *other things?* He doesn't have *other things*. He's a loser. That's what I liked about him.'

'C'mon. Get dressed. Let's go out, take a walk. Exercise is good for you.'

'That's just a myth started by PE teachers to force teenage girls to play netball when they're in pain.'

'Well, are you hungry? I bought a steak yesterday. We can split it.'

'I'm going to Daniel's in a bit,' she said, turning back to her film.

'Don't you think you should give him some space?'

In answer, she tugged off the joggers. The T-shirt reached half-way down her pale thighs. She pulled a battered Converse onto one of her bare feet and tied the laces. 'He can't just leave me fucked up and haemorrhaging,' she said. 'He can't. It doesn't make any sense.'

She stamped around the flat looking for her other shoe. A

slash of Lady Danger on her lips, mascara scabbed on her lashes, a gun-metal grey glitter around her eyes. She pulled on a battered leather jacket that she knew he hated.

'You look like you're going into battle,' I said. She looked nothing like the version of herself that she usually wore around Daniel – the girl who wore natural fabrics, make-up that took hours to look barely there, loose hair, no bra, bare feet, green juice, small appetite, wide eyes, open and curious and interested in listening to his world view, absorbing his ideas like a pretty little sponge.

She snarled and slammed the front door, and through the nets I watched her stalk down the garden path, hands jammed into her pockets.

I opened every window and door to air the heartbreak from the flat. I put on an upbeat playlist and played it through the Bluetooth speaker, then set about making dinner. I made a peppercorn sauce, sliced potatoes into hasselbacks and baked them in butter, salt and garlic. Finally, when I reached into the fridge for the sirloin, I found the plastic ripped open and a large half-moon bite taken from the meat.

She came home just before sunrise and climbed into my bed fully clothed, all cold leather and hard buckles from the leather jacket. She smelled of sweat, of blood, and of the buttercream scent of MAC lipstick. Drowsy, I pulled her arms around me, making myself the little spoon, and took her cold hands in mine. They were sticky.

'It was still beating,' she whispered into my neck. 'It felt like a fistful of worms. All those different muscles, all those veins and arteries, pulsing and contracting.'

A set of headlights rolled across the ceiling.

'Sophie,' I whispered. 'Sophie, what have you done?'

'Amazing, really,' she said, 'to think that such a complicated thing is just flesh.'

In the darkness, a heavy smell hung between us, a smell like raw hamburger meat. My stomach gurgled, and I realised I was hungry.

CREATURES OF HABIT

TERRI-JANE DOW

When I am at home at my parents' house, we eat mostly in silence. The only sounds are the soft scraping of cutlery against crockery, and the occasional faint mumble from the television at the other end of the room. We are hungry and we worry that our food will go cold with too much talk. We like to save the best bits until last, unless it is mashed potato, which my mum heaps so generously that there is enough to include some on every happy forkful.

My dad and I eat our dinner in the same order, methodically working our way clockwise around our plates, regardless of what is on them. As I eat, I wonder if this is a habit that anyone else has ever noticed. Did I pick it up in order to be more like him, something that started as sympathy? Is it symptomatic of sitting across the table from him, in the seat that is always mine, for thirty years? I wonder if we are truly the sum of the people we spend the most time with; an amalgamation, cut and pasted into a single self.

Growing up, the four of us – my parents, me and my younger sister – would split into two sets of two. Travelling for holidays, Mum and I sat behind Dad and Sarah, passing red pots of Pringles through the gap in the aeroplane seats. I couldn't be trusted to sit with either my sister or my dad for four hours; there would be too much giggling or bickering, depending on the mood. Conversely, on walks along the seafront after weekend drives to Southend-on-Sea, Dad and I would stride miles ahead of Mum and Sarah, eating chips out of newspaper wrapping. Having finished eating his own, Dad would steal my chips and then complain about the lack of vinegar.

Since he died, I have re-evaluated the difficult parts of our relationship. I've dug through my memory and investigated every argument, every time my teenage feet stomped up the stairs. I have replayed every single time a person in my life quietly uttered, 'You clash because you're so alike' – and there are many. Instead of a sigh, I hear it now as a mantra. I cling to what used to infuriate me: our matched, stubborn refusal to lose a fight. I have thought about how our shared flaws are also our strengths; about how every time I've been asked, in job interviews or uni introductions, who my role model is, I have answered 'my dad' without hesitation. In a million years, I would never have admitted that to him.

Perhaps I should have.

If we are a collection of the best parts of the people we are surrounded by, and I cannot be surrounded by him anymore, I am afraid that I will lose the parts of me that were parts of him.

Fussy eating is very common in children. It's difficult to define what exactly makes a child a 'picky eater', so numbers vary wildly between the studies that have been carried out. (There is a broad spectrum of disordered eating in children very separate to eating disorder diagnoses, though there is sometimes overlap.) Dislikes can include certain textures, colours, flavours and shapes, or can manifest in preferring liquid to solid food, or can show up as regression – a sudden disliking of previously enjoyed foods. Fussy eaters can have strong favourites, and equally strong dislikes, or distrust, of new or 'bad' foods.

For most children, fussy eating is a relatively brief period in their lives. The majority grow out of fussy eating soon after starting school, when new experiences become an almost everyday routine and, apparently, according to studies, only around thirty per cent of fussy habits last longer than two years. Parents of fussy eaters often report heightened levels of stress and fear, in both themselves and their children. I was fussy for far longer than two years.

I moved back home when I was twenty-eight, after ten years away, on and off, living in various cities and countries. When I returned, I was newly vegetarian, causing a spike of worry in my parents. A refrain of 'That would be better with a bit of chicken' tended to accompany my meals, but mostly they were glad that I was eating, and that my foodie requests were far easier to accommodate than they had ever been before.

At various points, starting from when I was three, I had gone through phases where I would exclusively eat only the following: Penguin bars (an excellent biscuit choice, though not quite an Australian Tim Tam, and not particularly nutritious); chicken dippers (not nuggets – there is an important distinction between coatings); Breville toasted cheese sandwiches, hold the cheese (yes, I am rolling my eyes too); Big Macs with just the burger patty (I still have no idea what McDonald's sauce is). Some of these phases lasted for years.

So far, the vegetarianism hasn't been a phase – I wasn't a very good meat-eater, despite having probably eaten a lifetime's worth of Bird's Eye chicken dippers (when you are a sixteen-year-old girl who will only eat chicken dippers, it takes a lot of chicken dippers to fill you up). I've never eaten anything on a bone, and I have eaten steak only once, when I was twenty-five, in a French restaurant where the waiter was so disappointed in my 'well-done' request that he actually shook his head when writing it down.

My dad enjoyed eating steak. If we were out somewhere nice for dinner, and he was feeling especially daring, it sometimes even came with a peppercorn sauce. I say daring, because ulcerative colitis and steak with peppercorn sauce are not friendly towards one another. Known to be exacerbated by stress, ulcerative colitis is a chronic inflammatory disease that affects the large intestine. There's no cure, but there are various management drugs, plans and treatments. In more serious cases, there are surgical options. My dad was diagnosed in his mid-twenties, so ill that when I was three months old he discharged himself from hospital so that he could die at home. My mum made him cut the grass instead.

One of the main management systems for colitis is diet plans, though there's no single diet that will suit everyone. Some people will be more inclined towards particular food triggers, and various food groups can cause flare ups at different times, so diets have to be flexible, despite being strict. The list of foods to avoid is extensive. It includes (though is not limited to) alcohol, dairy, spicy food, fizzy drinks, cereal, wholegrains, caffeine, nuts, meat, raw fruit, raw vege-tables, beans, popcorn, and sugar. Food has been a difficult topic in my house for a long time. Sometimes, dad couldn't eat at all for days. Or he might crave a takeaway, bored of being unable to eat, aware that KFC would cause another flare up. Steak and peppercorn sauce was a very rare treat. Perhaps my child-brain saw his not-eating and took it to heart. I wanted so much to be like him, and I am so much like him. Neither of us do things by halves.

He died two weeks before I turned thirty-one, of a 'massive upper gastrointestinal haemorrhage', while on holiday with my mum in Spain. Likely caused by thirty years of colitis damage and subsequent complications, we'll never be completely sure. Both the autopsy and death certificate are in Spanish, and there's nothing in his medical reports to suggest that we should have expected it. Ulcerative colitis is a life-challenging, rather than a life-threatening, disease. At the crematorium, we were given a piece of paper with his cause of death written on it in English, which my mum found in her handbag a couple of hours later.

Five of us had flown out, and after Dad's funeral, we went with my mum to the restaurant they had booked for the last night of their holiday. It was terrible. Everyone's meal arrived at the table wrong, went back to be rearranged, and came out wrong again. We had more dinners than people, no drinks, rogue side orders, bread that arrived and was immediately whisked away again. After we had explained twice that what had been brought over wasn't what anyone had ordered, we gave up and attempted to eat what we'd been given. It was all almost inedible. Heartbroken and mildly hysterical, we toasted an apology for coming to the restaurant that he had booked, without him.

I remember a family holiday, when I was maybe ten years old, walking along a strip of restaurants. It was a not-yet tourist-trap part of Spain in the mid-nineties, and children's menus were just smaller-portioned adult meals. There were no chicken dippers. There was fish, which the waiter promised would be deboned, or spaghetti pomodoro. I would not eat either, so we walked on to the next restaurant, where the same thing happened again. In my memory, we walked up and down for hours, until my little sister fell asleep and had to be carried. In my memory, Dad was more and more angry every time I shook my head, crying, hungry. In my memory, we went back to the apartment hungry, and mum made toast with the sweet, square, white Bimbo bread we bought in the supermarket, in our self-catering kitchen.

My memory is unreliable. There was rarely true anger; I just never saw how frustrating, how worrying, how difficult my eating was for other people.

Past a certain age, fussy eating is embarrassing. Navigating the awkwardnesses of being a teenage girl is difficult enough. In an all-girls' school, it's possibly more difficult. I was a late bloomer. I didn't get my first period until a month before my sixteenth birthday. I wore a ridiculous underwired double-A bra because the embarrassment of changing for PE without one was unbearable. Potentially, if I had been eating anything other than crinkle-cut microchips for weeks at a time, those things would have been different.

With something akin to shame, but not quite the same, I relive the hours I spent sitting at the dinner table, chewing until I physically couldn't swallow whatever it was I was trying to eat. I think about how, as an adult, I remember his face across the table being etched with worry – though for years I misunderstood it as anger – that I wouldn't eat. I remember the plates with dividers so that my food wouldn't touch; my excitement and pride, aged eighteen, at eating pasta with a stirred-through sauce for the first time. It had been a challenge I had set myself, completed weeks before I flew off to the other side of the world on my own, to show that I would be okay.

I remember calling my dad from a hostel somewhere along

the east Australian coastline, to tell him, horrified, that I had accidentally eaten kangaroo meat at a barbecue, disguised as a regular burger. He thought it was hilarious. He told everyone.

The most recent time I tried being vegetarian, the time it stuck, was a turning point. I was in Edinburgh, living in a city I loved, surrounded by people I loved. Most of those people were on the vegan/vegetarian/pescatarian scale somewhere, and all of us were too poor to buy meat. It was gradual, but easy. I was the happiest I'd been for a long time, and I didn't want every meal to be stressful any more. I wanted to enjoy eating. For the first time, I found myself asking only 'Is there a vegetarian option?' instead of obsessively googling menus and TripAdvisor reviews ahead of time, working out if there would be sauces mixed together, if there would be ingredients I didn't like, if there would be something I could eat.

I went to potluck dinners, I made salads (I'm still not great at dressing, but maintain that it's because I am English and it's too cold in the UK to eat good salads) and tried random dishes that other people had brought. For a while, a regular rota of Sunday night dinners meant that I ate other people's comfort foods, and learned how to make them my own. One week, a friend spent a small fortune on salmon, and baked it with a sticky mango sauce. At the table, she asked, worried, if I thought it was overdone. I had never eaten anything like it and told her it was incredible, a party in my mouth. She laughed at me, thinking I was mocking her.

On one of my parents' visits, I took them to a tucked-away restaurant I had been told was great. Dad grinned as the waiter set his enormous plate down in front of him, and his eyes widened as I poured gravy over my mountain of vegetables. It's one of my favourite photos of him. Badly lit and grainy from my camera phone in the dim lighting, it instantly transports me back to that meal – sitting opposite him, as I always did, with my mum beside me, keeping an eye on my plate.

I have thirty years of sitting opposite him at the dining table to remind me that the likenesses are in-built. After years of fighting them, I'm glad of them now. They are a part of my framework, something unchangeable, rather than something that I could reverse, with work, if I wanted to. Despite not seeing them reflected back at me, I won't lose those similarities.

At dinner, with his empty chair opposite me, I rotate my plate slightly, and pick up my fork.

LIFE IS STILL

SORCHA COLLISTER

Life is still
With peaches
Eaten on the streets
Of the Italian town
Four please from the market stall
A full-lunged
Deep smell
Of the warm skin
Washed
As you jump back from the splash
And you lean forward to bite
And slurp
And still it drips on your summer dress
And tickles your wrist
As it makes its way

From your sculpted hand
That has become as big as a Rodin
It knows it is the centre of that moment
The cathedral of your senses
The concentrated stillness
And the smile of
The sugar
That slips you down the street
And leaves you with
Sticky hands and
A simple moment

CONTRIBUTORS

In summer 2020, we held an open-submissions period for pieces of original creative writing by women on the subject of food. The incredible response confirmed our suspicion: that women writers had many, many stories to share about food. After reading more than 150 submissions, we chose the sixteen brilliant pieces you have read in this collection. *What She's Having* wouldn't exist without the words of the women below, and we are honoured, and so grateful, to publish them.

Ettie Bailey-King

Ettie is a writer and content strategist who helps charities to tell better stories. She co-runs the Schools Consent Project, a charity teaching sexual consent in England and Wales. She studied English Literature at Durham and Oxford universities, and has taught as a roving private tutor, a debating coach in prisons, juvenile detention centres and at Eton College. Her life highlight? Being bitten on the face, on a train in Siberia, by a monkey wearing trousers.

Tutku Barbaros | @TutkuBarbaros

Tutku is a writer – across forms – and performer from SE London. She is currently on the Sphinx 30 Lab creating new female-led work for the stage. She's also one third of company Plunge with whom she co-creates work for stage and screen.

Sorcha Collister | @sorchajc

Sorcha lives in London and works in the music industry. She was born and raised in the Isle of Man and there she grew up to love both music and poetry. She is published in London's *New River Press*, their two Yearbooks and their American release of 'Smear'.

Terri-Jane Dow | @terri_jane

Terri-Jane is a writer based in London. She co-manages Florence Welch's book club, Between Two Books, and is the editor of literary journal *Severine*. She has previously written for *Lucy Writers Platform*, *Chicago Review of Books*, *Oh Comely*, *Restless* and *Jellyfish Review*, among others.

Amy Feldman | amyrfeldman.com

Amy Feldman is an editor and has also written for *Vintage Life*, *National Trust Magazine* and Dear Damsels. She is the author of a number of National Trust guidebooks, *Cats of the National Trust* and *Dogs of the National Trust*.

Paula Hilton

Paula R. Hilton explores the ways even the smallest moments show us what it is to be human. Her fiction, essays and poetry have appeared in Dear Damsels, *The Sunlight Press*, *Feminine Collective*, *The Tulane Review*, *Smoky Blue Literary* and *Arts Magazine*, *Writing In A Woman's Voice*, *Kalliope*, *Ellipsis* and on NPR's *This I Believe* website. Hilton's debut novel, *Little Miss Chaos*, was selected as a Best Indie Teen Read by *Kirkus*. She recently published her first collection of poetry, *At Any Given Second*. She lives in Florida with her husband, son and daughter.

Candy Ikwuwunna

Candy Ikwuwunna is an aspiring writer, a huge pop culture obsessive, with a fondness for romance, women's fiction and teen dramas. She works in the third sector.

Ansa Khan

Ansa Khan is an editor and lives in London.

Hannah Lawrence

Hannah is a queer journalist and Yorkshire gal who recently discovered creative writing as a great way to while away time as she waits for her next meal.

Maria Ilona Moore | @mariailonamoore

Maria is London-based writer interested in language, memory and female-centred narratives. She has an MA in Creative Writing from Cardiff University and has been published by Dear Damsels and *F*EMS* zine. She also runs *Dear Movies*, a print zine about films and feelings.

Lucy Porter

Lucy Porter is a PhD student and civil servant. Her non-fiction has been published in the academic journals *Appetite*, *Preventive Medicine* and *BMC Public Health*, and her fiction by Dear Damsels, *Aesthetica* and *Norwich Writers' Circle*. She is obsessed with food, dogs, swimming, books, and rambling around London.

Grace Safford

Grace Safford is a writer and editor from a town in Northern Vermont so small cartographers sometimes confuse it for a lake. She's passionate about gardening, feminism, whales and wearing very ugly socks. You can find her work published or forthcoming in *Ghost City Press*, *Corvid Queen*, *Lucent Dreaming*, *Twist in Time* and *Fireworks*. Currently, she is working on her first novel and a writers' activity book.

Syeda Salmah

Syeda Salmah is a freelance writer who has been teaching English Literature and Language and Media Studies to her students for ten years. Born and raised in London, she is the eldest child and daughter of Bangladeshi parents who were invited by the government to create a new life in the

UK. She hopes that by writing about her diaspora experiences, she will encourage others to also take pride and solace in their binary identities.

Alice Slater | @alicemjslater

Alice is a writer, editor and podcaster from London. She co-hosts the literary podcast *What Page Are You On?*, reviews short stories for *Mslexia* and regularly chairs literary events at Waterstones and beyond. Her fiction has been shortlisted for the Bridport Prize and appeared in Dear Damsels, *Cunning Folk*, *Extra Teeth* and *On Anxiety* (3 of Cups Press). She also edited *Outsiders*, an anthology of short fiction from 3 of Cups Press.

E.V. Somerville | @evsomerville

E.V. Somerville is a spoken wordsmith, anthropologist and mischief-maker from south-east London. She is drawn to the overlooked, lost, peripheral and underestimated – that's where there's often magic to be found. E.V. has been writing non-fiction, short stories, poetry, zines, performance, diaries and world-renowned snail mail since she could hold a pencil.

Kate Young

Kate Young is an award-winning writer and cook. Her first book, *The Little Library Cookbook*, was shortlisted for the Fortnum & Mason's debut food book award and won a World Gourmand food writing award. Her second, *The Little Library Year*, was shortlisted for the Guild of Food Writers general cookbook award. Her third book, a celebration of Christmas, was published October 2020, and she is currently working on her fourth. Kate writes about food and books for various publications in the UK, and was Online Writer of the Year at the 2017 Guild of Food Writers awards. Originally from Australia, Kate now lives in the English countryside, making things, and exploring on foot.

ILLUSTRATIONS

Molly Alessandra Cooper | @mollyalessandra_

Molly draws people and writes about food in her spare time. She is co-founder of mishmash, a creative food website. Find them on Instagram **@mishmashfood**

THANK YOU

Long-term supporters of Dear Damsels will know that *What She's Having* was preceded by *Let Me Know When You're Home* – and without that book, this one just wouldn't exist. For that reason we wanted to use this space to thank those who bought, read, loved and shared *LMKWYH*. Your enthusiasm and encouragement meant that our hopes for a second book were able to become a reality.

While this is our second book, it's the first that we have published without crowdfunding. Even so, our readers got behind it from the very beginning, sharing the cover, pre-ordering their copy and generally spreading the word. The confidence this gave us in the project was (and continues to be) invaluable. We hope this book will enable us to make another, and another, for you.

As well as our incredible contributors (who, if you haven't already, you should flick back a page and read all about), we'd also like to thank photographer Libby Earland, for arranging a food-filled photoshoot and producing the beautiful cover image, and for all of the photography over the years; Marcus Chamberlain, for designing the perfect cover (that typeface!) and for turning this book into an actual book, and not just a Google Doc; and Kitty Stogdon, for her continued help, support and editorial wisdom.

Thank you!

FURTHER READING

Call Me By Your Name by André Acimen, Atlantic Books

Marie by Madeleine Bourdouxhe, Daunt Books

Home Cooking by Laurie Colwin, Fig Tree

Lamb to the Slaughter by Roald Dahl in *The Complete Short Stories: Volume One*, Penguin

The Gastronomical Me by M.F.K. Fisher, Daunt Books.

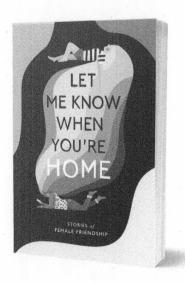

Let Me Know When You're Home:
Stories of Female Friendship

What is it that makes female friendship so special / complex / intense / important / messy / supportive / essential?

From growing up together to growing apart, from the oldest of friends to the fake ones, our relationships with other women can be our greatest loves. They can also be difficult, elusive and the source of our deepest heartbreaks.

In *Let Me Know When You're Home*, fifteen women writers look at female friendship in all its forms, in a collection of fiction, non-fiction and poetry that is both a frank exploration of these relationships and a true celebration of what women can achieve with the support of each other.

dear damsels

your words | your stories | your collective

deardamsels.com

🔲 deardamsels

🐦 deardamsels

📘 deardamsels